MISS LULU'S LEGACY

Stephen C. Shadegg has been a resident of Arizona since 1932.
Among his other published work:
The Miracle of the Salt River
The Phoenix Story - Century One
Arizona - An Adventure in Irrigation
Barry Goldwater - Freedom Is His Flight Plan
How To Win An Election
What Happened To Goldwater?
The Remnant (a political novel)
Winning's A Lot More Fun
Clare Booth Luce (a biography)

Arizona State University is pleased to publish this volume as part of its commitment to preserve the history of Arizona and the Valley of the Sun. The university finds it particularly valuable to record the history of medical services in the Valley since various ASU programs — including those in the College of Nursing, in the Department of Microbiology, and in the Center for Health Services Administration — have been established to help improve regional health care delivery systems.

MISS LULU'S LEGACY

Stephen C. Shadegg

Foreword by
Jack Williams

Published by
Arizona State University
Tempe, Arizona

Library of Congress Catalog Card Number: 84-45228

ISBN: 0-9611932-1-2

Edited by Dean Smith, Arizona State University

Book cover design by Al Camasto, Arizona State University

Art work and illustration layout by Tracey Sutton,
BioCommunications

Published in the United States of America.

Typeset by Access Composition Services

Printed by COL Press

Bookbinding by Roswell Bookbinding

DEDICATION

The characters in the drama which this book documents were for the most part quiet, unassuming, almost pedestrian, doing what they had to do because there was a need to be met. Submerging any animosities or differences which might have divided them in order to reach a common goal, they confronted a hostile environment and triumphed. They built a city where there was none before. They created those institutions which mark the progress of civilization. They paved the streets and planted the trees and flowers. They built the schools, ordered the courts of justice, and established the hospitals of mercy. It is to them this book is dedicated.

Servants of God

Pioneers of the West

Such as these

Made this Nation great

CONTENTS

FOREWORD

This is a saga of pioneer zeal conquering hostile nature — the drama of a small agricultural community on the banks of the Salt River desperately fighting heat and isolation to become a great metropolis.

As a lifetime resident of Phoenix, radio commentator, mayor, newspaper columnist and governor, I can say with some satisfaction I was here when much of what is recorded in this book took place.

Perhaps we were all too preoccupied with our daily chores at the time to recognize and fully appreciate what was happening in our city.

This is much more than a history of the growth of Phoenix. It is triumphant testimony to the courage and the vision of those men and women who created and bequeathed to us a legacy we take for granted.

Meet then the characters, the strong-willed men and women who gave so generously of their talent. They are all here. The entrepreneur who moved the capital of the territory from Prescott to Phoenix. The Sisters of Mercy who built the town's first hospital. The Episcopal priest who created St. Luke's, a living memorial to the wife who died from tuberculosis. And Miss Lulu Clifton, the "lunger" who started what is now SamCor.

You will meet the man who, in modern times, was the first to recognize the agricultural potential of the Salt River Valley land. You will discover what brought about the passage of the National Reclamation Act, upon which all our prosperity depends, and meet the men who were responsible.

There are some delightful anecdotes about the early doctors and a never before offered delineation of the development of a baccalaureate college of nursing at Arizona State University.

There's more, much more, to interest both native and new-comer. This is a history which needed to be written. When you have finished your pilgrimage through these pages, you will be rewarded with a much clearer understanding of how it is that from those very uncertain beginnings our community has grown.

Jack Williams
Governor of Arizona
1967 — 1974

ACKNOWLEDGEMENTS

Fifty years ago, Charles Becker and Lloyd Eisele were operating the Phoenix Holsum Bakery which their fathers had started
in 1884. They hired a young man just out of school to write and
present a narrative program on radio station KTAR.

Radio time was sold in quarter-hour segments. Story telling
on radio was popular. Because the Becker and Eisele families were
true pioneers, Charles and Lloyd decided their radio program
should tell the history of Phoenix and Arizona. It was called
"Tales of Pioneer Days," and it aired three times a week for almost three years. This was the beginning of a vocation which has
occupied my major attention for half a century.

In those early years there was as much interesting historical
fact to be found in the memories of the surviving old timers as
there was available in the written histories.

I cultivated the friendship of Vernon L. Clark and George H.
Maxwell, two men who played leading roles in the creation of the
water storage system which makes it possible for men to survive
in this valley on the northern tip of the Sonoran Desert. Joseph
Kibbey was gone, but two of his law partners, Judge Frank O.
Smith and John L. Gust, gave generously of their time to contribute to my understandings of what took place in those months immediately preceding the passage of the National Reclamation Act.

Charlie Stauffer and Wes Knorpp were publishers of *The Arizona Republic and The Phoenix Gazette*. They opened the files of their newspapers and encouraged my efforts to gather information. Perhaps they tolerated my endeavors because their own roots were so deeply embedded in the early days.

Lin B. Orme, Bill Pickrell, and Rod McMullin of the Salt River Valley Water Users' Association made available all the early documents of that organization and then fleshed out the dry statistics with their personal recollections.

William Oscar Sweek was the first doctor I met when I came to Phoenix. Howell Randolph and his wife, Josephine, were active members of the Phoenix Little Theater, where I directed and produced plays.

Maie Bartlett Heard, who contributed the converted stable which was our playhouse on East McDowell Road, became a supporter, perhaps because her close friend and confidant, Vi Driskell, was one of the company's most accomplished actresses.

James M. Barney, who graduated from Stanford and devoted much of his life to researching the history of Arizona, opened his files to me. Mulford Windsor, who was then State Librarian, helped me gather much material which had never been recorded. Publisher and then Governor Sidney P. Osborn, whose grandfather gave the land for the original town site of Phoenix, added to my understandings of the past. There were other old timers, too numerous to mention, to whom I am deeply indebted.

When Stephen M. Morris first suggested there might be a story in the history of the development and growth of Good Samaritan Hospital, the notion was immensely appealing. I saw it as an opportunity to bring to life those men and women who were responsible for the magnificent inheritance we take too much for granted these days. In completing this project, which has occupied most of my time for the past eighteen months, it has been necessary to dispel some myths. For example, the assumption that the Deaconess Hospital commenced operating in a building at 215 North 12th Avenue. And to validate others. The generous contribution of the Mormon Church at a time when the hospital was in dire financial straits.

For their contribution to these pages, I am deeply grateful to Stephen Morris, Sherman Hazeltine, Robert Creighton, Lucille Brown, Richard Smith, Edith Sexson Faville, Carol Angeny Goodson, Vurlyne Boan, Milt Coggins, Mary Jane Knorpp Harwood, Mrs. Tessie Morley, Allen Rosenberg, Loretta Anderson Hanner Bardewyck, Milton Gan, Leslie Weight, John Hughes, Frank L. Snell, Grace Middlebrook, Helen Ellis Shackelford, Charlotte Buchen, William O. Hendricks, Director of Research of the M. H. Sherman Foundation, Bill Shover, who opened the files of *The Arizona Republic* to my research assistants, Lois Boubong and Antoinette Nelson, Doctors L. D. Beck, Hank Running, Gordon Shackelford, Paul Jarrett, Dermont Melick, Merlin Kampfer, Paul Singer, and Brian Lockwood, Orme Lewis, Carolyn Durkin, Joe Prekup, C. A. Carson III, to Ellen Roach, who typed and retyped the manuscript, and to Dean Smith, talented writer for *The Arizona Republic*, now at ASU, whose editing skill contributed immensely to the readability of this book.

Stephen C. Shadegg

CHAPTER 1

In The Beginning

In the first year of the 20th Century, Phoenix was a dusty village at the northern tip of the Sonoran Desert. The economy was dependent upon irrigated agriculture. Thirty years earlier the first farmers had constructed dams of rock and brush to divert the water from the flowing Salt River into ditches to be spread across the land.

Three years of drought, beginning in 1897, forced more than half the farmlands to be abandoned. Flash floods in 1900 damaged or destroyed all of the diversion dams. Many of the early settlers gave up, moved on. It appeared a hostile nature had triumphed.

Eighty years later, Phoenix is the ninth largest city in the United States, with a thriving, prosperous metropolitan population of more than one and one-half million. Farming, mining, and cattle raising, the mainstays in territorial times, have been replaced by manufacturing and tourism.

In 1911 Miss Lulu Clifton, a deaconess of the Methodist Church, established a hospital in a rented building at 750 West Taylor Street. Seventy years later, "what Miss Lulu started" is a multi-hospital organization serving seven communities and a population of two million. It is now a system offering the most advanced medical and surgical services, demonstrating that the economies of scale reduce the cost of quality health care.

The same courageous, determined, resourceful men and women who conquered the threat of flood and drought also were involved in the growth and development of this hospital system. The events are inextricably entwined. Complementary. Interdependent. In the past, we find our future. If in 1910 anyone had dared to predict what is reality today, he most certainly would have been dismissed as a foolish visionary.

Those pioneers who came to the frontier West developed a wonderfully strong sense of community. They were involved with and dependent upon their neighbors for survival. Even short distance travel was hazardous. The hostilities of nature were as life-threatening as the marauding Indians, who deeply resented the white man's coming. Neighbors made the isolation a little more bearable but, at best, life was difficult. The men, women, and children, forced to rely on their own resources, were fiercely independent. At the same time they shared their neighbors' problems, cooperated as if their lives depended upon it — as in fact they did. What threatened one threatened all: Indians, outlaws, flood, drought. When challenged they responded with a unity demanded by their situation.

Contrary to western fiction, "gambling, whiskey and wild, wild women" held little attraction for the settlers. Sunday church was the big event in their lives, starting with Sunday School for both adults and children, then a worship service, and often a potluck supper in the evening. The women spent long hours to be sure the family was dressed in clean clothes for Sunday. There were church-sponsored baseball games and trips by buggy and wagon to the falls on the Arizona Canal. With creature comforts so limited, it was easy to understand why a cherished hope of Heaven meant so much to these pioneers. They made the church the center of their lives.

Chroniclers of the westward tilt to the Sun Belt sometimes suggest cities such as Albuquerque, El Paso, Denver, Tucson and Phoenix just lucked out. They credit the benign climate as being responsible for the growth in population and commercial activity.

In this Arizona portion of the Sun Belt the growth came as a result of imaginative, almost visionary planning, with considerable risk taken by the early settlers and their successors.

In the 19th Century, the pioneers who entered and settled the territory west of the Mississippi River can be separated into five categories, each with a separate cast of characters and singular motivation.

First came the scouts, the mountain men, the trappers — restless adventurers uncomfortable in the settled East — men such as Bill Williams, Kit Carson, Pauline Weaver, James and Sylvester

Pattie. Some had book learning. Some were illiterate. They trapped the beaver, killed the buffalo, outwitted the hostile Indians, traded with the friendlies, and were inexorably drawn to cross the next horizon.

The scouts broke the trail for the gold hunters, most of whom went on to California hoping to find fortune and then return to the place of their origin. The trappers and traders, the gold hunters, were transient.

In the third group came the tillers of the soil — land seekers intent on putting down roots, establishing new homes. They rode through Arizona in their covered wagons headed for the fertile valleys of California and Oregon. Some of them recognized the opportunity on the banks of the river Salt and traveled no farther.

The merchants, doctors and lawyers were not far behind. They came to serve the settlers or the Army posts established to protect the pioneers from the Navajo and Apache, who were not about to give up their lands without a struggle.

And finally came the health seekers — the "lungers." Tuberculosis was the dread disease sometimes referred to as "consumption" or "lung fever." Doctors did not know what caused it or how to cure it. There was a theory that fresh air, sunshine and mild winters could delay the progress of the disease — might even cure the sufferer.

Lulu Clifton was a "lunger," one of a vast number of men and women who came to Arizona, were cured of their affliction, and remained to build and to shape the destiny of this raw frontier community.

In 1902, the year before Miss Clifton arrived in the Salt River Valley, President Theodore Roosevelt signed the Hansbrough-Newlands Act, more familiar today as "The National Reclamation Act." This single piece of legislation, the foundation for irrigated agriculture in the West, has created more wealth than all of California's gold, Colorado's silver and Arizona's copper combined. And here, in Central Arizona, the systems constructed under the Hansbrough-Newlands Act have made it possible for the city of Phoenix to become the ninth largest city in the United States.

When that legislation was signed into law Phoenix had been a place of permanent habitation for only 35 years. Centuries earlier the land had been occupied and farmed by the long-vanished Hohokam. Traces of that earlier civilization, recognized by former

Confederate Captain Jack Swilling, inspired the beginnings of this modern-day city.

Swilling was one of those dispossessed by the War Between the States to come west seeking a new beginning. He joined the Walker Party and helped mine for gold in the Lynx Creek area south of Prescott. When Heinrich Heinzel, who is known to history under his assumed name of Henry Wickenburg, made his rich strike at the Vulture Mine, Swilling came south hoping to participate in that bonanza.

The ore from the Vulture was crushed in crude arastras constructed on the banks of the Hassayampa River. The settlement took the name of the man who had struck it rich. But Henry Wickenburg never profited from his discovery.

On September 7, 1865, the Army established Camp McDowell, a military post on the east bank of the Verde River above its confluence with the Salt. It was the only permanent habitation in the Salt River Valley. The cavalry horses required feed. A civilian, John Smith, who worked as hosteler at the fort, entered into a contract to cut the wild hay which grew along the flowing Salt River and transport it to Camp McDowell.

In all the histories of Arizona, this pioneer is identified as "John Y. T. Smith," but, when he hired Swilling, he was plain "John Smith." Years later, when he was a prosperous mill owner and a member of the Territorial Legislature, Smith persuaded that law-making body to legally change his name to "John Y. T. Smith." No one knows what the initials stood for, if indeed they stood for anything, but they separated the bearer of that new name from all the plain "John Smiths" in the territory.

In 1866 Smith hired Swilling to help him cut the hay and drive a wagon across the 30 miles of desert to the military fort. At times, when the Apaches were raiding, it was hazardous work. For the most part it was tedious, monotonous labor.

In his trips across the Valley, Swilling recognized what he correctly assumed to be the remnants of an ancient canal system constructed to carry water from the river to the surrounding Valley land. The wild hay was abundant proof of the land's fertility; there were soldiers and miners to be fed.

In 1867 this ex-Confederate soldier, miner, Indian fighter and teamster recruited a company of 11 men and, in a small adobe house on the banks of the Hassayampa at Wickenburg, the

Swilling Ditch Company was organized, with capital of $400 in cash, some horses, wagons, plows and scrapers.

The first attempt to tap the river's flow — at a point where the river is now bridged at Tempe — failed because the diggers encountered rock. The second effort, a mile or two downstream, succeeded, and in 1869 these settlers planted corn and wheat and irrigated their crops with water from the Salt River.

The success of this early venture inspired other men to construct additional ditches on both sides of the river. Diversion was accomplished by building crude dams of rock and brush, forcing the water into the entrance of the ditch.

By 1888 there were 11 diversion canals — including the most northerly and largest, appropriately named the Arizona, financed and constructed by W. J. Murphy. Almost 200,000 acres of Valley land was made green. The future appeared to be assured.

Murphy came to the Salt River Valley in 1882. He was 42 years old and had spent the prior two years grading the roadbed across parts of Nebraska, Colorado, New Mexico and Arizona for the Atlantic and Pacific Railroad, which ultimately became the Santa Fe. All of the other canals then diverting water from the Salt River had, in general, followed the path of the prehistoric ditches. Murphy selected a diversion point almost 20 miles east of the city, about where Granite Reef Dam is now located. He had engineers design his ditch. It was almost 70 feet wide at the top and 50 feet at the bottom. It stretched more than 40 miles, from just below the confluence of the Verde and the Salt to the Agua Fria on the west. It was designed to provide water to approximately 70,000 acres never before irrigated. It was Murphy who planted the ash and olive trees which grace North Central Avenue all the way to the canal he built.

Prior to that first great flood in February of 1900, the future of Phoenix had seemed assured. Irrigated agriculture was becoming more important to the territory than mining or cattle raising. Phoenix, centrally located, was attracting a new class of residents — capitalists, businessmen, financiers.

In 1889 by an act of the 15th Legislature, the territorial capital (first located in Prescott, then moved to Tucson, then moved back to Prescott) was permanently established in Phoenix.

Both Prescott and Tucson were older communities. Prescott wanted to retain the capital. Tucson wanted it back. But the growing economic importance and the central location of the new little community on the Salt River, surrounded by 200,000 acres of fertile farmland, could not be ignored.

Phoenix businessmen, prodded into action by Moses Hazeltine Sherman, made the Legislature "an offer it couldn't refuse." Sherman, the largest taxpayer in Maricopa County, promised to donate ten acres of land between Adams and Jefferson Street at 17th Avenue as a site for a new territorial capitol building. He also promised to construct a street railway from the downtown area to the proposed capitol.

Moses Hazeltine Sherman was born December 3, 1853, in West Rupert, Vermont. He was distantly related to John Sherman, the puritan clergyman; to Roger Sherman of Revolutionary War fame; and to the brothers John and William Tecumseh Sherman. He attended Oswego (New York State) Normal School and was subsequently appointed principal of the Hamilton New York Union Grade School.

In 1869 President Ulysses S. Grant appointed A. P. K. Safford governor of the Territory of Arizona. Safford is remembered as "the father of Arizona schools." He also had the territorial legislature pass a bill granting him a divorce.

In 1873 Governor Safford persuaded Moses Hazeltine Sherman to come to Arizona. Sherman was suffering from tuberculosis. There is no record to indicate that Safford and Sherman had ever met, nor is there anything to explain why the territorial governor selected this consumptive teacher to open the first public school in Prescott. But somehow the arrangements were made, the governor advanced funds to pay for Sherman's trip to the territory and he commenced his teaching duties in the Fall of 1873. Sherman's health improved. The population of Prescott increased. And, in 1876, the town built a new two-story schoolhouse, described as "the best in the territory." Sherman was named principal.

Governor Safford resigned in 1877, and a year later President Rutherford B. Hayes appointed John C. Fremont as Safford's replacement. Fremont named Sherman Arizona's first superintendent of public instruction. In 1880 the legislature made the post elective, and Sherman was voted into office.

An able administrator and an excellent teacher, Sherman drafted the Territorial School Laws and helped persuade Congress to appropriate 72,000 acres of public lands for the support of education in Arizona. This trust still exists and continues to benefit the public schools.

Sherman's great talent was as an entrepreneur — a promoter. He moved to Phoenix, acquired property and was involved with W. J. Murphy in building the Arizona Canal. With Colonel William Christy, he was one of the founders of the Valley Bank of Phoenix (not to be confused with the present Valley National Bank). He formed a partnership with General M. E. Collins, and together they subdivided farm land for residential purposes: the University Addition on West Van Buren north of the Town Ditch, the Capitol Addition, and the Collins Addition east of Seventh Street.

The personal correspondence of General M. H. Sherman — "General" because his friend, Governor Fremont, had once named him Adjutant General of Arizona — preserved at the Sherman Library in Corona Del Mar, California, sheds some new light on what the history books say about the moving of the capital.

Prescott was served by a spur line of the Santa Fe Railroad, which came south from Ash Fork. Phoenix was connected to the main line of the Southern Pacific by a spur road at Maricopa, but stagecoach or horseback were the only means of transportation between Phoenix and Prescott.

The history books say Sherman put together a travel fund — contributions collected from Phoenix businessmen — and offered to pay the railroad fare and provide entertainment for any members of the legislature who would go to Los Angeles on the Santa Fe, and then come back to Phoenix on the Southern Pacific.

Train travel was a luxury many of the members of the legislature had never sampled. John Y. T. Smith was Speaker of the House. When the 15th Territorial Legislature opened its first session January 21, 1889, Smith introduced House Bill 1, "An act to locate the capital of the Territory of Arizona permanently in the City of Phoenix and the County of Maricopa." The measure passed. The legislators enjoyed their junket, and Phoenix achieved a new importance.

Most of the funds to promote this change came from the railroads. The Southern Pacific was particularly interested in gaining access to the freight being developed by the Valley's farmers. Correspondence in 1888 between Sherman and J. A. Muir of the Southern Pacific Railroad indicates that Sherman was the railroad's Arizona lobbyist. In one letter he suggests the railroad give passes to the Honorable N. A. Morford, editor of the *Phoenix Daily Herald.*

On March 30, 1889 Sherman wrote again to Colonel J. A. Muir saying, "The legislature is over. The capitol bill passed. I expect the new capitol building will be erected in the center of a tract of land I own just west of town. I shall run my street railway to it and boom it with all my power. When we get things in shape, I'll send you a deed to a couple of good lots. Thanking you for your kindness. . ."

The correspondence in Sherman's letter file reveals he was only a part owner of the land where he proposed to locate the capitol. The ten acres to be offered was to come out of a 40-acre piece owned jointly by Collins, Sherman and J. W. Strevell, of Miles City, Montana. To acquire it, Sherman had put up $1,000, Strevell $4,000. This had been paid to Collins, the original owner, who retained a one-quarter interest in the 40 acres.

A copy of an unsigned letter addressed to Strevell in the Sherman file, probably written by Colonel Christy of the Valley Bank, explains precisely how the deal was made to put the capitol building in its present location. The legislature had named three commissioners to select a proper site for the new capitol building. The letter says these three were all close friends of M. H. Sherman.

There were others interested in donating land for the capitol. One group offered ten acres just north of Van Buren, the then city limits, between Seventh Street and Seventh Avenue. Another group proposed to locate the capitol on the southern city limits, just south of Harrison Street. Either one of these locations would have been much closer to the center of town. The letter says sponsors of these proposed locations had offered the commissioners a bonus of some lots adjacent to the site they proposed. Apparently Sherman topped that offer. He and Collins gave each of the commissioners five acres of ground immediately adjacent to the ten acres on 17th Avenue, which they proposed as the location of the capitol.

The *Phoenix Daily Herald,* whose editor was a friend of Sherman's, supported the 17th Avenue location and, according to a story in that newspaper's edition of July 8, 1889, Sherman and Collins promised to extend the streetcar line to the capitol grounds, to open a 100-foot roadway around the site and to plant 500 shade trees.

The commissioners chose the 17th Avenue site. Collins and Sherman conveyed ten acres to the Territory as a gift, but there were strings attached. Should the land not be used as the location of the capitol, it would revert to the heirs of Sherman and Collins.

Prices for lots in the Shaw Tract quadrupled in value when the commissioners announced their decision. The speculators made a handsome profit, and the commissioners were amply rewarded for their good judgment. Sherman built a handsome residence at 13th Street and Washington. He promoted the development of East Lake Park by extending the street railway tracks east on Washington to 16th Street. The publicly-owned park attracted riders to the railway system. Sherman built his streetcar line out Grand Avenue to serve the Christy property and the territorial fairgrounds. On most occasions when he extended the car line, land promoters who were being served contributed handsomely to the cost of expansion.

Sherman moved from Arizona to California, where he developed the Pacific Electric Railway System, organized the National Bank of California, subdivided what is now Hollywood, and became closely associated with General Harrison Grey Otis and his son-in-law, Harry Chandler, of *The Los Angeles Times.*

It was M. H. Sherman who persuaded his cousin, William Emory Hazeltine, to move to Prescott from Cincinnati, Ohio. Will Hazeltine became involved in the organization of the Bank of Arizona on August 11, 1877. He was named Cashier in 1882 and became part owner in 1888. He persuaded his younger brother, Moses B. Hazeltine, to come to Prescott, and in 1896 Moses Hazeltine assumed management of his brother's holdings.

Years later Moses Hazeltine contributed his financial acumen to help solve the financial problems of the organization Lulu Clifton started: The Arizona Deaconess Hospital. And after Moses Hazeltine retired as a trustee, his son Sherman served on the board from 1960 to 1971.

The need to construct a permanent water storage system had been recognized before the floods of 1900 and the four years of drought at the end of that decade. It was not the lack of rain in the Valley, where the annual average is less than eight inches, which threatened the settlers. The Verde, the Tonto and the Salt Rivers drain a combined watershed of 24,320 square miles — a land area larger than the states of Connecticut, New Hampshire, Massachusetts, and Rhode Island combined. Both the Tonto and the

Verde flow into the Salt. The melting winter snow, the spring and summer rains, are the foundation of the Valley's past and present prosperity. A water storage system could control the flow of the river in wet years and conserve enough in a storage reservoir to carry the farmers through the dry years.

In the summer of 1889 the Maricopa County Board of Supervisors authorized W. M. Breakenridge, James H. McClintock and J. R. Norton to search the upper reaches of the Salt and Verde Rivers for a suitable reservoir site.

William Milton Breakenridge — "Colonel Billy" — a native of Wisconsin, had been a deputy sheriff in Cochise County when the Clantons and the Earps shot it out at the OK Corral in Tombstone. He moved to Phoenix and was named County Surveyor.

James McClintock was born in Sacramento, California. In 1879, when he was 15 years old, he came to Arizona where his brother Charles E. McClintock was publisher of the *Phoenix Daily Herald*. He was graduated from the Normal School at Tempe, then worked for his brother's newspaper. In 1885 he became a civilian employee in the Adjutant General's Office at Fort Whipple. This was at the time of the Army's campaign to capture Geronimo.

In April, 1898, McClintock, Alex O. Brodie and William O. "Buckey" O'Neill enlisted a cavalry regiment which is known to history as Roosevelt's Rough Riders. Seriously wounded, McClintock recovered and returned to Arizona to become Colonel of the First Arizona Infantry. In 1902 his old commander Theodore Roosevelt — now President — appointed him Phoenix postmaster.

McClintock's three-volume *History of Arizona*, published in 1914 and now out of print, is highly regarded as a reliable source of information about the early days. John R. Norton, an associate of Colonel Christy and W. J. Murphy, was superintendent of the Arizona Canal Company.

With their surveyors' instruments, their food, bedding and cooking utensils lashed to the back of pack mules, McClintock, Breakenridge and Norton made their way through the steep canyons of the Salt River. They found a number of possible locations for a dam and a storage reservoir and finally agreed on a site 76 miles from the Valley, where Tonto Creek joins the Salt River. Here the combined waters passed between two high hard rock abutments where a dam could be anchored securely. They thought the Lower Tonto Basin could hold all of the water the Valley would ever need.

The report prepared by Breakenridge, Norton and McClintock was forwarded to the Senate Committee on Irrigation and Arid Lands. United States Senator William Morris Stewart of Nevada brought his committee to Phoenix. A mass meeting was held at City Hall, at which Senator Stewart publicly approved the practicality of the project. But nothing happened.

Arthur P. Davis, an engineer with the U.S. Geological Survey, came to verify the findings of the Breakenridge committee. He visited the site, returned to Washington and declared the proposed dam and storage reservoir eminently feasible from an engineering standpoint.

The problem was money. In 1890 the population of Phoenix was 5,544. It was estimated it would cost more than $10 million to construct the dam, build a road to the remote location and complete the necessary diversion structures. The total assessed valuation of Maricopa County was a little less than $10 million, and territories were prohibited by federal law from going into debt.

How the city men, the farmers and the politicians responded to this disastrous situation offers an explanation of the continuing growth and advancement of this community and its institutions. It illuminates the character and displays the courage of those men and women who built the West.

Colonel William Christy was a distinguished veteran of the Civil War. When the hostilities were over, he entered the banking business. He was then elected State Treasurer of Iowa, a post he held for four years. He was Director and Cashier of the Capital City Bank of Des Moines and then helped to organize the Merchants National Bank.

In failing health, Colonel Christy came to Prescott, Arizona, in 1882. A year and one-half later, his health recovered, he moved to Phoenix and purchased 440 acres west of the city. He brought the first white-faced cattle into Arizona and he planted the first citrus trees. In 1883 Christy helped to organize the Valley Bank of Phoenix.

The Christy home and the Christy farm were on Christy Road, an extension of McDowell Road west of 19th Avenue and the fairgrounds. When W. J. Murphy built the Arizona Canal Christy was vice-president of the company. It was Christy who first suggested a method for financing irrigated agriculture which eventually became the public policy of the United States.

Representative Francis Newlands of Nevada was a trustee of the Sharon Estate of Nevada, which owned a substantial block of stock in the Valley Bank of Phoenix. Newlands came to Phoenix because of his interest in western reclamation and because of his concern over the Sharon Estate's investment. His Arizona contact was Colonel Christy, the bank's president.

As the West developed, money from the sale of public lands flowed into the U.S. Treasury. Colonel Christy proposed that some of these funds be made available for the construction of dams and water systems in the West. Government loans would be secured by a first mortgage on the lands benefited. As the funds were repaid they could be used to finance additional irrigation projects.

The U.S. Congress was dominated by easterners. Christy recognized these men, who knew little of the West, had no experience with irrigated agriculture, and would probably resist any proposal to make funds available from the federal treasury. But he suggested they might agree to earmark a portion of those funds derived from the sale of public land. Newlands thought the proposal had great merit, but he doubted the Congress or President McKinley would support the plan.

The Phoenix Board of Trade, encouraged by Territorial Governor Alexander O. Brodie, developed a different approach. The people would petition Congress to permit Maricopa County to issue bonds to be sold to private investors to secure the necessary capital. The Board of Trade sent Benjamin Austin Fowler to Washington, D.C. to seek congressional approval for the county bonding proposal.

Fowler, a native of Stoneham, Massachusetts, served in the Union forces during the Civil War. He was graduated from Yale in 1868, taught school for a time, and was then engaged in the publishing business in Boston, New York and Chicago.

Fowler contracted tuberculosis and came to Arizona as a health seeker in 1899. By 1901 he had recovered sufficiently to seek and win election to the 21st Territorial Legislature.

After three months in Washington, Fowler was ready to admit defeat. He had been unable to enlist any support for the county bonding proposal and he was ready to return home.

If any one man can be credited with the passage of the National Reclamation Act, George Hebard Maxwell is that man. Maxwell was born in Sonoma, California. In 1882 he was admitted to the California Bar and commenced to practice law with a partner, William J. Mesick. The firm specialized in mining law. In his personal memoirs Maxwell said his share of the firm's income that first year was $24,285 — a princely sum at that time.

Maxwell's fascination with irrigation and water law began when he was retained by a group of California farmers who were being forced to pay for water they did not receive. Maxwell became a fervent evangelist for reclamation. He virtually abandoned the practice of law, and in 1899 he organized the National Reclamation Association. He formed an alliance with Senator Newlands of Nevada and was in Washington when Fowler arrived. Maxwell persuaded Fowler to give up the county bonding proposal and join him in lobbying for the passage of the Hansbrough-Newlands Act.

Newlands had teamed up with Senator Henry Clay Hansbrough of South Dakota. Together, with Maxwell's help, they drafted a bill along the lines first proposed by Colonel Christy.

On September 6, 1901, President McKinley was assassinated in Buffalo, New York. Theodore Roosevelt became President of the United States. Although born in the East, Roosevelt had come west as a young man because of a health problem. He favored the idea of reclamation and particularly the legislation Newlands and Hansbrough had prepared.

Arizona's Territorial Governor Alexander Brodie had been a member of the Rough Riders recruited by Teddy Roosevelt to fight in the war against Spain over Cuba. Brodie and the new President were close friends. The governor went to Washington to urge Roosevelt to support the reclamation legislation. In his first message to Congress President Roosevelt recommended the adoption of the Hansbrough-Newlands Act and the promotion of reclamation in the West.

There was a flaw in that act as originally drafted. It proposed that "monies coming into the federal treasury from the sale of public lands in the West be used for the development of reclamation projects on public land." George Maxwell discovered the language — which would have limited the benefits of the act to public lands — and persuaded Newlands and Hansbrough to put a comma after the word "public" and insert two words, "and private."

Many, many years later it was George Hebard Maxwell who persuaded the board of trustees of the Arizona Deaconess Hospital and Home to change its name to Good Samaritan.

The passage of the National Reclamation Act provided the means but not the method for rescuing the water-short farmers in central Arizona. The money would be available only if the communities applying were united — only if the proposed local organizational structure satisfied federal demands — and only if the owners of all the lands to be benefited agreed to grant the federal government a first lien on their land.

A dam and a reservoir at the Tonto site offered the promise of salvation to the lands in the Valley below. But the people were not united. Owners of water rights established in the early 1870s objected. They said the dam would benefit the Johnny-Come-Latelies, whose water rights had not been perfected until the 1880s. Owners of large acreages objected to the 160-acre limitation imposed by the National Reclamation Act.

Joseph H. Kibbey had served as governor of the territory and justice of the territorial supreme court. He was at the moment probably the most highly respected lawyer in Arizona. Sponsors of the project engaged Kibbey to write the articles of incorporation. What he produced became the model for all reclamation projects.

As judge, Kibbey had established the principle of prior appropriation and of appurtenant water rights. The water, he said, belonged to the land and was inseparable from it. For the land owners it was an extremely onerous prospect: to surrender their prior water rights to the association and mortgage their land to the federal government.

In 1937 Judge Kibbey's law partner, John Gust, an active supporter of that hospital Lulu Clifton started, commenced 12 years of service on the hospital's board of trustees.

Colonel Christy, John P. Orme, Vernon L. Clark, B. A. Fowler, James McClintock and others argued that prior appropriation rights were worthless if there was no water in the river. They said the amount of the federal mortgage would easily be paid off once there was an assured water supply.

After a period of uncertainty, the owners of more than 240,000 acres of land agreed to the terms of the mortgage and subscribed to the articles of the Salt River Valley Water Users Association. B. A. Fowler was named as first president of this, the Nation's first reclamation project.

A part of it was luck. President McKinley was not in favor of western reclamation. His successor, Teddy Roosevelt, was. The fact that Governor Alex Brodie and James McClintock had helped recruit the company of Rough Riders Teddy Roosevelt led in the war against Spain gave them access to the President. Additionally, Senator Newlands and B. A. Fowler had been classmates at Yale. Winston Churchill once said that luck was largely being in the right place at the right time.

A contract for the construction of Roosevelt Dam was awarded to the John M. O'Rourke Company of Galveston, Texas, on April 8, 1905. On March 8, 1911, ex-President Theodore Roosevelt came to Arizona to dedicate the dam which is named in his honor, and the future of the Salt River Valley was assured.

CHAPTER 2

Lulu Clifton's Dream

Lulu Clifton was a "lunger." When she arrived in Arizona in 1903 she had only three assets: the name of the pastor of the First Methodist Church, Reverend A. M. Gibbons; $12.50 in her purse; and the faith to believe that if God had a further purpose for her on this Earth, He would help her conquer tuberculosis. She was 34 years old.

Her father, Charles Wesley Clifton, fought on the side of the Union with Company C, 138th Iowa Volunteers. When the war was over he returned to the family farm at Havelock. The memories of the brutality of the Civil War prompted him to enter the ministry. He was ordained by the Northwest Iowa Methodist Conference in 1870, a year after his first child, a girl christened Lulu, was born. The Church operated a training school for City, Home and Foreign Missions in Chicago, where girls — who could not enter the ministry — were prepared to serve the church as deaconesses.

Beautiful, slender, brown-eyed Lulu Clifton graduated from this school after three years of study and was assigned as a deaconess to work in the lower income factory neighborhoods at Fall River, Massachusetts. Deaconesses were expected to be missionaries, evangelists, social workers and family counselors. The young girl from Iowa did all these things and did them well.

From Massachusetts she was sent to Nebraska, where she served as field secretary for the Deaconess Hospital of Omaha. In her fourth year at that post she contracted tuberculosis. By the time her illness was diagnosed it had made alarming progress. Her doctors were not encouraging. They said the dry climate of Arizona might be beneficial, but they did not think she would survive the long train trip.

Miss Clifton was engaged to be married to Edmund Bristow, an ordained Methodist minister who had been assigned to the missionary field. Lulu's illness made marriage impossible, so the engagement was broken. Alone, desperately ill, her dreams of the future shattered, the little deaconess set out for Arizona.

Lulu Clifton may have come west on the Santa Fe to Ash Fork and then down the spur line through Prescott, Skull Valley and Wickenburg to Phoenix. Or perhaps on the Southern Pacific to Maricopa Junction and then across the Gila and Salt on the Maricopa and Phoenix spur line. The main lines of the two great transcontinental railroad systems had bypassed this unimportant capital city of the Territory of Arizona.

The population of Phoenix was less than 5,000. The streets were unpaved. There was only one hospital, St. Joseph's, operated by the Sisters of Mercy. But there were numerous small establishments, private sanitariums dedicated to the treatment of respiratory diseases — a treatment consisting primarily of rest and abundant fresh air offered on screened porches and in tents.

Pastor Gibbons helped Lulu Clifton find a place to stay. She lived in a tent, cooked her own meals, cared for herself. The Methodist deaconesses in Nebraska sent her enough money each month to cover her expenses.

Alone, without family or friends other than Pastor Gibbons, exhausted by the paroxysms of coughing which no active tubercular can escape, terrified by the amounts of bright red blood the coughing produced indicating further hemorrhaging, Lulu Clifton refused to give up.

Dr. Mark Rogers of Tucson, writing in the *Medical and Surgical Reporter*, described the conditions of life Miss Lulu was forced to accept. "No one will dispute the statement that the outdoor life is the one for the consumptive. By outdoor life I do not mean that the patient is to spend a few hours each day in the open air, to return indoors when he becomes a little fatigued. I mean that he should remain in the open air as do the cattle, which are turned out to graze day and night for weeks and months at a time."

Those first years she was too ill to leave her tent house to attend worship services. Some members of the Methodist congregation who had learned of her from Pastor Gibbons came to see her, bringing gifts of food and reading material. She corresponded regularly with some of the deaconesses she had known in Nebraska; particularly with Marilla B. Williams, a registered nurse. Those who knew her say Lulu was never despondent and exhibited a lively interest in the community. If God wanted her to live, she would live.

As the months passed, the warm, dry air worked its miracle of healing. Miss Clifton moved to a little rented house at 326 North Third Avenue, bought a horse and a buggy, and resumed her work as a deaconess, calling on the sick and the poor, teaching in the Sunday School, serving others. In these years of her convalescence the mood of the community, thanks to the passage of the National Reclamation Act, had changed from one of anxious uncertainty to optimistic confidence.

Between 1900 and 1910 the population of Phoenix more than doubled and Lulu Clifton thought about what she could do with the life God had given back to her. Considering her background and her problem of personal health, the choice was obvious. This growing little city needed a second hospital — a Protestant hospital. Not that she found any fault with the institution on Fourth Avenue operated by the Sisters of Mercy. She just thought there ought to be another place where broken bones could be mended and diseases treated.

The Sisters of Mercy came to the American West in 1854 and to Arizona in 1892. Sisters Mary Peter and Mary Alacoque were teachers. Phoenix was a haven for health seekers but there was no hospital. The sisters petitioned their superiors to permit them to establish a hospital and, with the support of the pioneer business community, they succeeded. St. Joseph's was opened in a small converted residence near the corner of Fourth Street and Polk in 1895, with six rooms and 12 beds.

The practice of medicine was primitive. Many of the doctors had never attended a medical school. The Board of Medical Examiners of the Territory was offering an examination as early as 1897, but not all those who called themselves doctors and treated the injured and the ill bothered to take that test. The Maricopa County Medical Society had been organized in 1892 by Doctors Henry A. Hughes, Logan D. Dameron, William H. Ward and Ancil E. Martin.

The operating table at St. Joseph's consisted of a seven-foot pine board, two feet wide, placed on two sawhorses. Only two types of anesthetic were known — ether and chloroform. They were poured directly from the bottle onto a towel and administered to the patient. There were no surgeon's caps, masks, gowns or gloves. The doctors rolled up their sleeves, washed their hands, put on rubber aprons to protect their clothing, and did the best they could. And their best was pretty good.

Six rooms and 12 beds were totally inadequate to meet the community's needs. A year later the hospital was moved to another location on Fourth Street. The new building had 24 rooms. In 1901 an annex was built to provide space for an operating room, a diet kitchen, a utility room and more patients. In 1910 the Sisters established the first school of nursing in Arizona.

St. Joseph's has continued to grow and expand to meet community needs and still is one of the leading hospitals in the West, with 88 years of continuous service to the health needs of the people.

In 1907, Reverend J. W. Atwood, rector of Trinity Church, a small Episcopal mission in Phoenix, opened a church-sponsored sanitarium named St. Luke's Home. Atwood's wife Anna had contracted tuberculosis when they were stationed in Columbus, Ohio. He had accepted the mission post in Arizona hoping the climate would benefit her health. She died in 1907. Atwood spent that spring and summer touring Episcopal congregations on the East Coast soliciting funds so that he might help others suffering with the dread disease. He raised about $6,000, with which he purchased four acres of desert land at Van Buren and 18th Street.

Atwood wrote, "We bought a dozen secondhand tent houses. I hired a young seminarian, Bertrand R. Cocks, whose wife was tubercular, to oversee the new venture. Cocks built the administration building and we opened at Christmas time, 1907. The tent houses accommodated 20 patients, who were charged $12.00 a week for their room, board and medical care."

Cocks served as superintendent of St. Luke's for 34 years. The Reverend J. W. Atwood became missionary bishop of the District of Arizona. Today St. Luke's Medical Center is one of the great hospitals of the Southwest.

There is no record of just when Miss Lulu Clifton recovered sufficiently to think about resuming her duties full time as a deaconess of the Methodist Church or when she decided to organize the Arizona Deaconess Hospital and Home.

Roosevelt Dam was nearing completion. The assessed valuation of Maricopa County had doubled since 1900. There were three first class hotels — the Commercial (Luhrs) at Central and Jefferson, the palatial Adams at Central and Adams, and the Ford at the corner of Second Avenue and Washington.

The Overland Telephone and Telegraph Company at 246 West Adams, with Frank T. Alkire as treasurer and C. R. Snowdon as manager, served the businesses and some of the residential area. The exchanges were Main, Black, Red and Green. The Pacific Gas and Electric Company — no connection with the present giant utility on the Pacific Coast — distributed power within the city limits. All the downtown buildings and most of the residences had electricity. S. D. Lount and Son manufactured ice. Frank Luke, whose son Frank Luke, Jr. became Arizona's hero in World War I, was county assessor. Dwight B. Heard operated his real estate investment and insurance company from a building at the corner of Center (Central) and Adams and lived in a magnificent residence, the Casa Blanca, on Center Street north of McDowell Road.

There were five banks and 14 churches. Carl Hayden was Sheriff of Maricopa County. The New York Store owned by Sam and Charles Korrick and the Boston Store owned by the Diamond family were both on Washington east of Center. At the corner of Center and Washington, Salim Ackel offered general merchandise. Across the street the Phoenix Bakery, operated by Ed Eisele and Alfred Becker, filled the morning air with the delicious aroma of fresh baked bread and rolls. At First Street and Adams, Goldwater's featured the latest in fashions from New York and Paris.

Big Mike Goldwater, a Polish immigrant, had brought the name to Arizona in 1860, driving a peddler's wagon across the deserts from California. At various times there were Goldwater mercantile establishments at La Paz, Ehrenberg, Prescott, Bisbee and Phoenix. Baron Goldwater, big Mike's youngest son, who had opened the Phoenix store in 1896, married Josephine Williams, a young trained nurse from Nebraska who, like Lulu Clifton, contracted tuberculosis and was sent to Arizona as a last resort. The first child of that marriage, Barry, who was born New Year's Day, 1909, is now known to all the world as United States Senator Barry Goldwater, the Republican candidate for President in 1964.

The First Methodist Church, originally established in a small 30-foot by 50-foot red brick Gothic building at the corner of Second Avenue and Washington on May 22, 1881, had been torn down to make way for the Ford Hotel. A magnificent new church building had been erected at Second Avenue and Monroe to serve the growing congregation. Church records reveal the cost of land and building at Second Avenue and Washington in 1881 was $4,000. When the original church was ready to move, the builders of the Ford Hotel paid $15,000 for the land — a pattern of appreciating real estate values which still persists.

Dick Smith, former Phoenix city councilman, state fair executive, banker, and for many years Arizona manager for Fox West Coast Theatres, has a very clear memory of Miss Lulu Clifton. "Almost everyone in our Sunday School class was taller than she was. But she stood so straight and had such a presence we never thought of her as little. She was a good teacher. She always wore a long black taffeta skirt, a white shirtwaist tied at the throat with a thin black or white ribbon and a long-sleeved short-waisted jacket. I don't know if this is what deaconesses were required to wear, but I never saw her in any other clothes. Her hats were all alike and they covered her hair. But when she smiled you knew she loved you, and she was smiling most of the time."

Lucille Brown, whose parents Jacob and Laura moved to Phoenix from Jerome in 1909, remembers that Miss Clifton never called any of the members of the congregation Mr. and Mrs. "It was Brother Brown and Brother Christy. All the ladies were Sister but she used their given names. My father had tuberculosis. Miss Clifton came to see him at least once a week. I remember her saying, 'Brother Brown, I was much sicker than you are when I came here. Now I'm well and soon you will be well'." Lucille Brown says Miss Clifton was a great comfort to her family (Lucille's father *did* recover from tuberculosis).

In 1909 the Reverend Robert S. Fisher was called to Phoenix to serve as pastor of the First Methodist Episcopal Church on the northwest corner of Second Avenue and Monroe. Half a block to the east on the same side of the street a new building was under construction to house the Young Men's Christian Association. The "Y" had been organized in 1892, with Colonel William Christy as first president and Dr. J. C. Norton as recording secretary. In 1907 a drive for capital funds headed by B. A. Fowler, Dr. Norton, Colonel William Christy and his son Lloyd raised more than

$103,000 in eleven days — a remarkable achievement for a community which just seven years earlier had been facing a very uncertain future.

The success of this first YMCA fund drive was of greater significance than it might appear to a casual reader of the community's history. After the passage of the National Reclamation Act and the growing national awareness of the benefits offered health seekers by Arizona's climate, a new class of individuals migrated to the Salt River Valley. These were professional men and successful businessmen, who brought substantial capital resources with them — men such as Dwight B. Heard, K. S. Townsend, W. J. Murphy, William Christy and Dr. Ferdinand G. Angeny.

The youngest child of a well-to-do Pennsylvania Dutch family, Ferdinand Angeny graduated from the University of Pennsylvania Medical School in 1892, entered private practice and then returned to the University to serve as chief instructor in the Medical School's Department of Surgery. In 1907 he contracted typhoid fever from one of his patients and then was stricken with pneumonia. He was advised to find a warmer climate and came to Phoenix with his wife, who was pregnant. Mrs. Mel Goodson (Carol Angeny), the issue of that pregnancy, remembers her mother telling her they first lived in a house on Indian School Road where the cooking was done on a wood stove and the family slept out of doors under the umbrella trees in the summer. The Indian School location, considered to be "out in the country," was served by a streetcar line. The track, which came north from Washington on Fourth Street and then jogged over to Third Street at Roosevelt, terminated at Indian School Road.

After one summer "in the country," Dr. Angeny found his health much improved and he moved his wife to a house on North Third Avenue. During his convalescence the doctor had become acquainted with Dwight B. Heard. They were both enthusiastic tennis players. A builder by the name of William H. Patrick had started construction of a two-story masonry building at 215 North Third Avenue. Dr. Angeny decided to locate permanently in Phoenix. He bought the unfinished building and had it completed to his specifications — eight double rooms with a full basement, with additional living quarters on the first floor and a space for the doctor's medical office. Completed in mid-1908, it became the second hospital in this rapidly growing community. The building was in the heart of downtown Phoenix, a block from the First Methodist Church and the YMCA, the site of the new Federal Courthouse and the Salt River Valley Water Users' Association administration building.

At that time there were 33 doctors of medicine to serve a Phoenix population of a little over 11,000 — or a very high ratio of one doctor to every 333 residents. This is probably because a great many of these 33 doctors, like Angeny, had come west to recover from some health problem and the Salt River Valley had acquired a national reputation as a place where "lungers" had the best chance of survival.

When Lulu Clifton recovered from her tuberculosis she went back to work as a deaconess for the Methodist Church in Arizona. But what she really wanted to do was to organize and establish a health care facility under the direction of the deaconess organization. She found an enthusiastic ally in William Christy's son.

Lloyd Christy was an officer in the Valley Bank and a community leader. He was also superintendent of the Sunday School at the First Methodist Church. He, too, had a personal reason for being particularly interested in the health needs of Phoenix. In 1893, while attending the World's Fair in Chicago, he contracted typhoid fever. For a time doctors despaired of his survival. He was nursed back to health by Miss Lunette Ready. During that convalescence Christy spoke in glowing terms of the beauty of Arizona and a year later, when Miss Ready graduated from training, she decided to come west. Christy and his brother George met her in Wickenburg, where the Santa Fe spur line terminated, and drove her to Phoenix in a buckboard. Lunette Ready was the first graduate nurse in Phoenix.

In 1909 Lloyd Christy was elected Mayor, succeeding Colonel Lewis W. Coggins. Coggins, an active member of the Baptist Church and a Republican, had been elected on a reform ticket in 1906. During his administration the city put an end to the gambling houses which had operated since the early days of the settlement, acquired a municipal domestic water system, and built the first concrete sidewalks.

Coggins, who was born in Lamoine, Maine, came to Phoenix in 1892, formed a partnership with Z. O. Brown, and entered the land abstract and title business.

In 1910 there were three title and land abstract companies — the Valley, organized in 1887 by William Christy; the Phoenix

Title Guarantee, organized in 1897 by S. A. Dysart; and Coggins and Brown, in the abstract business since 1892.

Henry Bannister Wilkinson, a graduate of Northwestern University's Law School, came to Phoenix to practice his profession in 1898. In 1910 he persuaded the owners of the three existing title and abstract companies to merge. Having three title firms maintaining separate records was wasteful, he argued, so on February 3, 1910, lawyer Wilkinson filed the articles of incorporation for the Phoenix Title and Trust Company. The papers were signed by L. W. Coggins and Lloyd B. Christy. Wilkinson became the first president of this new financial company which, in subsequent years, grew to dominate the title business in Arizona.

Dwight Bancroft Heard, who came to Phoenix in 1897 because of ill health and remained to play a vital leadership role in the growth of his adopted state, was a member of that first board of directors of Phoenix Title. Heard was the founder of the Bartlett-Heard Land and Cattle Company which developed 7,500 acres south of the Salt River. He was owner and publisher of *The Arizona Republican*, active in the movement for statehood, a close friend of President Theodore Roosevelt, and came within 800 votes of being elected governor of Arizona in 1924.

When the city of Phoenix was incorporated under the leadership of John T. Alsap in 1881, the boundaries were Seventh Avenue on the west, Seventh Street on the east, Van Buren on the north and Harrison on the south: one-half section, 320 acres. Alsap was a graduate of the College of Medicine in New York and practiced in California for ten years before coming to Arizona in 1864. He was also a lawyer, and here he practiced law, not medicine. By 1900 the city limits had been expanded to 19th Avenue on the west (if Phoenix was going to be the capital of Arizona it would not do to have the capitol building outside the city limits), 12th Street on the east, Roosevelt Street on the north and Yavapai on the south between Seventh Avenue and Central, a total land area of about two and one-half sections.

Between 1900 and 1910 the city limits were extended on the west to 23rd Avenue between Van Buren and Harrison, on the east to 16th Street between Van Buren and Harrison, and on the north to McDowell Road from Central to 12th Street.

Dr. Angeny's new facility on Third Avenue was a welcome addition to the community's health resources but it was a one man affair. Lulu Clifton had been associated with the Methodist deaconess hospital in Omaha. She thought the Methodists and the other Protestant churches should share the burden of providing hospital care. What she proposed was the establishment of a deaconess hospital to serve the people in the Salt River Valley. A number of influential community leaders agreed with her. Lulu Clifton wrote to her old friend Marilla Williams, the registered nurse she had known in Omaha who was also a Methodist deaconess. She said she was planning to organize a deaconess hospital in Phoenix and needed help. Miss Williams came to live with Miss Clifton at 326 North Third Avenue.

On October 18, 1911, Lulu Clifton's dream became a reality. The articles of incorporation of the Arizona Deaconess Hospital and Home were filed with the County Recorder. The incorporators were Lloyd Christy, an officer in the Valley's largest bank and the Mayor of Phoenix; H. B. Wilkinson, president of the title company; Reverend Robert S. Fisher, pastor of the First Methodist Church; S. J. Rogers, presiding elder of the Church; and G. H. Adams, Arizona's first presiding Methodist elder. Named to the board of trustees were C. T. Hirst, Dr. John Dennett, Jr. (one of the town's leading physicians), J. A. R. Irvine (son of a prominent merchant), Warwick Scott, Dr. J. C. Norton (one-time Territorial Veterinarian, land owner, developer and a leader in the YMCA), Frank Stewart, and Mrs. Louis Chalmers (wife of a prominent attorney).

The articles established that there would always be a majority of Methodist laymen and clergy on the board of the new organization. The first annual meeting was held October 19, the day after the filing of the articles.

A spacious residence at 750 West Taylor Street was leased. In the beginning it was more of a home than a hospital. Marilla Williams was in charge of the nursing staff and the board had plans for bigger and better things.

An article appearing in *The Arizona Gazette*, June 21, 1912, describing the new organization and its aims, says, "The present plan involves the construction of a wing to accommodate about 25 patients at a cost of approximately $20,000, to be followed later by the construction of a $50,000 building. . . ."

The newspaper story continues, "The first question confronting the promoters of any enterprise is invariably 'Why?,' but the answer to the 'why' for a Protestant hospital in Phoenix is so apparent as to need little argument. The growing population of the

Salt River Valley, the great number of health seekers among the people coming to the Valley, and the inability of the present hospitals to care for the increasing number of patients are all facts apparent to everyone.

"The deaconess movement of the Methodist Episcopal Church offers a means of administration of a Protestant hospital both economical and efficient. It is economical in that deaconesses are unsalaried, asking only comfortable support while in the work, and relief in sickness. It is efficient in that they are trained for service and selected on account of special fitness for the place each is to fill. The mark of approval of the church is seen in the costume they wear and in the license given by the church."

The same article lists twenty hospitals throughout the nation operated by the deaconess' organization.

The following year the hospital acquired some property on Tenth Avenue between Van Buren and Polk, adjacent to ten acres owned by the Arizona Wesleyan (Methodist) University.

By the end of 1912, in October or November, Dr. Ferdinand Angeny, who had found the practice in Arizona too primitive to meet his exacting standards, decided to return to Avon By The Sea, New Jersey, and leased the building at 215 North Third Avenue to Mrs. Ruth Elizabeth L. Hanson.

The *Phoenix Directory* for 1912 lists the Deaconess Home at 750 West Taylor. In the 1913 *Directory* the Deaconess Home is listed again at 750 West Taylor, and the property at 215 North Third Avenue is listed as "The Sanitarium." In the 1914 *Directory* the building at 215 North Third Avenue appears as "The Phoenix Hospital," Mrs. M. G. Dill, Manager.

Apparently Ruth Hanson and Mrs. Dill were not equal to the task of continuing what Dr. Angeny had started. In 1915 the doctor came back to Arizona to visit with friends and to do something with the hospital property.

During the time Angeny had been in Phoenix he had formed a close friendship with K. S. Townsend, a capitalist who had come to Arizona from Illinois in November, 1906 because of his wife's health. Carol Angeny remembers a dramatic event which she says really cemented the relationship between her father and Townsend.

"There was a flood in 1912 and the only way to get to the south side of the river was to crawl across some distance on a 12-inch plank. I don't know what held the plank up or how far you had to crawl, but I do remember that when Mr. Townsend's two nephews were ill with typhoid fever my father crawled across that plank with his medical bag, and stayed south of the river until the water went down. Mr. Townsend credited him with saving his nephews' lives. Townsend was very active in the Methodist Church. He told my father about a lady — I thought she was his sister because that's the way he referred to her — who had organized a new hospital and really didn't have a proper building.

"Mr. Townsend introduced my father to this lady. It was Miss Lulu Clifton. The Arizona Deaconess Hospital had the full support of the Methodist Church. My father was delighted to have a reliable tenant capable of using the building for the purpose it was intended, and since K. S. Townsend was on the board of the hospital along with Lloyd Christy and H. B. Wilkinson and a number of other friends of my father's, he was sure he would get his rent."

It was a providential arrangement. The building Dr. Angeny had designed as a hospital was returned to its intended use. The Deaconess Hospital and Home had been struggling to survive in inadequate, makeshift facilities. It had been a hospital in name and purpose. It now became a hospital in fact, with the building to support its mission. In 1915 "what Miss Lulu had started" moved from the Taylor Street location to the Angeny building on Third Avenue.

That initial effort to raise funds for a new $10,000 building to be constructed near Tenth Avenue and Van Buren had not been a complete success, but it was not a total failure. The hospital had acquired title to two acres on Tenth Avenue between Van Buren and Polk and had concluded an arrangement to acquire the ten acres then owned by the Arizona Wesleyan University. The hospital board of trustees had been immeasurably strengthened by the presence of K. S. Townsend. The building committee, headed by Mrs. Louis Chalmers, had not given up. But times were difficult.

Undaunted by that initial failure to raise funds for a new building on West Van Buren, Miss Clifton bought a small house at 215 North 12th Avenue, directly south of the ten acres where the proposed new hospital would be built. Only the Town Ditch, which ran along the south side of Van Buren Street, separated Lulu from that hospital she intended to build.

CHAPTER 3

World War I

In those beginning years, when Miss Clifton and her board of trustees were doing their utmost to raise funds for the construction of a new hospital, a number of events - local, national and overseas - complicated their task.

The assassination of the Austrian Archduke Francis Ferdinand by a Serbian terrorist on June 28, 1914, resulted in World War I and the U.S. was ultimately drawn into the conflict.

A change in women's fashions destroyed a substantial segment of the Arizona economy.

The Valley Bank of Phoenix failed.

An outbreak of hoof and mouth disease closed the Chicago stockyards.

The influenza epidemic of 1918 terrorized the population and underscored the need for expanded hospital facilities.

On February 14, 1912, Arizona was admitted to the Union as the 48th state. Statehood was the second great milestone in the people's quest for political equality with the rest of the nation.

Prior to February 24, 1863, Arizona was a part of the Territory of New Mexico. On that date, as a result of some very clever manipulation by Charles D. Poston, President Abraham Lincoln signed a bill creating the new and separate Territory of Arizona.

Poston was an early day pioneer who once operated a model mining community at Tubac and discovered the copper deposits at Ajo. He was sent to Washington along with Granville Oury of Tucson to petition the Congress to divide the Territory of New Mexico, which had been ceded to the U.S. in 1848 and augmented by the Gadsden Purchase in 1853, into a separate territory. Both reason and logic supported the proposal. The territorial capital of Santa Fe was more than 400 miles from Arizona's central valley. Effective administration of the land area, 234,829 square miles, from a single seat of government was virtually impossible. The Arizona portion of the territory was becoming increasingly important economically. But logic and reasoning had very little to do with the decision to divide the land area and create the new territory.

Poston invited a group of "lame duck" congressmen who had lost their seats in the election of 1862 to an elaborate oyster dinner party at the old Willard Hotel in Washington, D.C., remembered in history as the place where Julia Ward Howe wrote the "Battle Hymn of the Republic." After dinner Poston explained that the creation of Arizona as a separate territory would necessitate the appointment of a territorial governor and a host of other officers. He said President Abraham Lincoln was agreeable to naming these defeated members of Congress to the federal openings in the new territory.

With the help of their friends in Congress, these "lame ducks" secured the passage of the enabling act. President Lincoln signed it and promptly appointed John Addison Gurley, a three-term Ohio congressman, Governor. Gurley died before he could take office and President Lincoln appointed another lame duck, John Noble Goodwin of Maine, as his replacement. The people of Arizona celebrated the news and the name of Charles D. Poston was entered into the history books as the "father of Arizona."

As citizens of a territory, the people could not vote for president. Their governors were all political appointees named in Washington, as were the judges. The congressional delegates they elected had no vote in the national legislature and the authority of the territorial legislature was severely restricted. What the settlers wanted was statehood and, commencing in 1872, they repeatedly petitioned the Great White Fathers on the Potomac to admit them as brothers and equals. Forty years later, at ten o'clock on the morning of February 14, 1912, Republican President William Howard Taft signed the proclamation admitting Arizona into the Union as the 48th state.

The reason for the long delay was purely political. A majority of the people who had settled in Arizona prior to 1910 were from southern states, strongly partisan members of the Democratic Party. Republicans controlled the Congress and the White House for most of the years Arizona was seeking admission. There was an eastern bias against the West. A proposal to admit Arizona and New Mexico as a single state might have carried had it not been for the opposition of the people of Arizona.

By 1910 the economic importance of Arizona and the growth in population, exceeding that of New Mexico, made statehood inevitable. A proposed constitution, written in convention by 52 elected delegates and approved by the people February 9, 1911, contained three provisions which President Taft had warned would make the document unacceptable. These were the recall of elected officials, including judges; and provisions providing for initiative and referendum, populist proposals which Taft thought contravened the basic structure of a representative democracy.

Just as Charles Poston had utilized the self-interest of his "lame ducks" to secure the passage of the territorial enabling act, the people of Arizona accepted the reality of Taft's opposition and deleted the recall of judges from their constitution. After admission, the First State Legislature voted to restore the recall provision, referred it to the voters, and it was adopted. They also referred a measure proposing to give women the right of suffrage and that, too, was adopted. According to the 1910 census there were 206,297 people in Arizona. But fewer than 16,000 voted on the adoption of the State Constitution and only about 20,000 voters decided the question of women's suffrage.

In 1912, the women of the world who were wealthy and stylish, and some who were not so wealthy, adorned themselves with the feathers of the ostrich. They wore ostrich plumes in their hats and draped ostrich boas around their necks. In Central Arizona the raising of ostriches for their plumage was big business.

The ungainly, ill-tempered birds thrived in the desert climate. It has been estimated that when the plumes were in fashion the ostrich population of Central Arizona exceeded seven thousand. These two-toed birds, native to Africa, are eight feet tall at maturity. They cannot fly but it is said they could outrun a horse were it not for their tendency to run in circles. They defended themselves against aggressors with a powerful forward kick. The pioneer Pickrell family had an ostrich farm on North Central and Judge Robert Pickrell remembers being told his grandfather was kicked unconscious by an unruly ostrich.

Ostrich plumes went out of style with the outbreak of World War I. The farmers had a product they could not sell. The birds and the pens were a total loss. At the time about 750 acres of valley land were occupied by ostrich farms. The value of the birds, which suddenly became worthless, has been estimated at more than $2,800,000. The loss in annual income was more than $500,000.

German U-boats disrupted Atlantic shipping and Arizona's producers of short staple cotton could no longer ship to the mills in England. An outbreak of hoof and mouth disease closed the Chicago stockyards; hundreds of head of cattle in Arizona had to be destroyed.

The loss of Arizona's overseas cotton market when the Atlantic shipping lanes were interrupted had an unintended beneficial consequence. Automobile tires were manufactured with long staple cotton from Egypt. When Firestone and Goodyear, two major producers, could no longer buy the long staple variety from overseas they came to Arizona, acquired huge tracts of land and commenced cultivating the long staple Egyptian cotton here.

Paul Litchfield, who was to become president of Goodyear, purchased land west of Phoenix and created the community now known as Litchfield Park. Thomas Clements, vice-president and comptroller of the Firestone Tire and Rubber Company, came to Arizona and leased acreage near Chandler to grow long staple cotton for Firestone. He remained in Arizona and became associated with the Phoenix Title and Trust Company, which H. B. Wilkinson started.

On Saturday, November 8, 1914, the Valley Bank of Phoenix, which Colonel William Christy had founded in 1883, was closed by order of the State Banking Controller. The bank had 9,200 depositors, $306,000 in capital and in surplus and $1,965,850 in deposits. E. J. Bennitt was the bank's president; Lloyd Christy, its cashier; and, some of the most prominent businessmen in Phoenix were on its board, including H. M. Kennedy, John R. Hampton, E. B. O'Neil, P. T. Hurley, J. A. Cashion, and Baron M. Goldwater.

There were many reasons for the bank's failure, all of them the result of the vigorous role the bank had played in developing the economy of the Salt River Valley. Historian Ernest J. Hopkins, in his book on banking in Arizona, said if the Salt River Valley had outstripped other parts of the Southwest in the rounded character of its economy, as it had, the fact went back historically to the leadership of the Valley Bank of Phoenix.

The bank had financed many of the ostrich farmers, cattlemen, and cotton growers. It had loaned 85 percent of its deposits. The bank had some securities but the New York Stock Exchange was closed as a result of an emergency war measure. And when a bank in California in which the Valley had $75,000 on deposit failed, the Valley was forced to close. Fifty-one days later it reopened as a new corporation, with new capital, rescued by the officers who owned the Gila Valley Bank and Trust Company.

The tragedy might have been a disaster had it not been for the leadership of some of the major depositors. A meeting was held, presided over by Dr. J. C. Norton. President Bennitt and Lloyd Christy, who suffered the biggest losses when the bank closed, put up $37,500 each and the other directors contributed $12,500 each, for a total of $150,000. As a result of the reorganization, most of the depositors suffered no loss at all and the new Valley, under the new management, became in time the largest bank in the Rocky Mountain region.

In spite of his great personal financial loss, Christy remained as chairman of the board of trustees of the Arizona Deaconess Hospital and Home, and it was he who signed the lease for the Angeny property on North Third Avenue.

Under the capable supervision of Marilla Williams, the number of doctors on the staff increased and plans went forward to build a new and modern hospital. The city was growing north and east, influenced to a considerable degree by the expansion of the street railway system.

The Methodist Episcopal Church and the Methodist Episcopal Church South were not divided on faith and practice. The separation came about as a result of the War Between the States and was maintained because of sectional and cultural differences. In 1917 the trustees of the Methodist Episcopal Church South made a gift of five acres to the Arizona Deaconess Hospital and Home Association. The land was located between 10th and 11th Streets, bounded on the north by McDowell Road and on the south by Brill Street.

The trustees who signed the deed were J. A. R. Irvine, who was also a member of the Deaconess Hospital and Home trustees; rancher W. L. Teal, and Dr. Logan Dameron, one of the medical pioneers who had formed the Arizona Medical Association. The land had been used by the church as a country camp. Because of the growth of the city it was no longer desirable for this purpose.

The hospital board had been strengthened with the addition of Judge J. C. Phillips and Professor John D. Loper. Phillips had been Probate Judge in Maricopa County and a senior partner in the prestigious law firm of Phillips, Cox and Phillips. In 1928 he became the second Republican governor chosen by the people of Arizona.

John D. Loper, a graduate of Northern University of Ohio, came to Arizona in 1896 and was Superintendent of Schools in Mesa. In July of 1909 he was made superintendent of the city schools in Phoenix. Phillips was a Methodist, Loper a member of the Christian Church.

In 1918 there were two former mayors of the city of Phoenix on the Deaconess Hospital Board of Trustees, Coggins and Christy; a powerful member of the State Legislature, H. B. Wilkinson; Probate Judge Phillips; community leaders Dr. J. C. Norton, K. S. Townsend, Levi Young, the Reverend Ray C. Harker, Dr. John Dennett, Professor J. D. Loper, James Aldrich, J. A. R. Irvine, Frank R. Stewart, Warwick Scott; and two women, Mrs. Louis Chalmers and Lulu Clifton.

The efforts of the Deaconess Hospital building committee were beginning to bear fruit. The location on McDowell Road, which had been much too far out in the country when the hospital was first organized, was now recognized as an ideal location for the projected new hospital building.

The construction of the Brill Street streetcar line on 10th Street, between Roosevelt and Thomas Road, led to the development of a preferred residential district in the area. The first governor of Arizona, George Wiley Paul Hunt, lived in a magnificent house just east of 16th Street on McDowell Road.

Hunt was elected governor of Arizona eight times. The first Republican to be elected governor, Thomas E. Campbell, lived on McDowell, as did Probate Judge John C. Phillips, who was elected governor in 1928, and Rawghlie Stanford, who was elected governor in 1936. Those who selected the 10th Street and McDowell location for the new hospital made a perceptive choice.

The Arizona Wesleyan University, under the sponsorship of the Methodist Episcopal Church, had acquired ten acres on West Van Buren Street between Ninth and 10th Avenue in 1912 and then leased the land to the fledgling Deaconess Hospital for one hundred years at the rate of one dollar per year. In 1917 the University gave this land to the Deaconess Hospital.

For a time in 1918 it appeared that Miss Lulu Clifton's dream of a modern hospital adequate to serve the needs of the Phoenix community under Protestant administration would become a reality.

There was a ground-breaking ceremony on the McDowell site and construction was commenced on plans prepared by V. O. Wallingford, a local architect. But the world was at war. The meager funds raised by the building committee were exhausted and construction was stopped with only the first floor in place.

The need for additional hospital beds was clearly evident. At the height of the influenza epidemic every health care facility in Phoenix was stretched beyond capacity. A temporary shelter was erected adjacent to the Third Avenue location and that 15-bed facility had as many as 30 patients at one time. The Women's Club house was converted into a makeshift hospital. St. Joseph's accepted 60 additional patients in its new tubercular ward. The State Health Officer, Dr. Orville Harry Brown, called for the cancellation of the Arizona State Fair. Social gatherings were forbidden. Theatres, schools, even the bars were closed. In November, 1918 notices were published in the daily press ordering all persons to stay home unless out on essential business matters. Anyone walking the streets was expected to wear a flu mask and the quarantine was enforced by the Sheriff's office and the Phoenix Police. The public schools were closed for 12 weeks and the "epidemic" took precedence over all other events, including the signing of the armistice which ended World War I on November 11, 1918.

Five years later, at four o'clock in the afternoon of Sunday, June 24, 1923, Miss Clifton's dream became a reality. The Arizona Deaconess Hospital and Home dedicated a fine new building built to the plans and specifications of architect Wallingford — plans which had been greatly enlarged since that first false start. The cost was more than $300,000. The new building had a special obstetrics section and delivery room with the first incubator in Arizona. There was a surgery wing with five operating rooms, a special X-ray section, and a hospital pharmacy. The day the hospital opened it had provision for 105 patients and could accom-

modate 140 in the event of an emergency such as the 1918 flu
epidemic.

It was Miss Lulu Clifton's dream but J. O. Sexson, with the
support of a great company of community leaders, had made it
possible.

CHAPTER 4

James Oscar Sexson

In the summer of 1911, James Oscar Sexson was 31 years old. He had a lovely wife, Daisy, and two small children. He owned the largest general merchandise store in Gosport, a trading center for the farmers in southwest Indiana. He also had asthma.

The doctors did not know much about this affliction, but a change in climate was believed to be beneficial. They told J. O. he probably would not survive if he stayed in Indiana. They recommended Prescott, Arizona.

Leave his friends and the familiar surroundings of the place where he had been born and grown up? Sell his store, give up the sense of security his efforts had earned for him? Travel two thousand miles to a strange place so new and so wild it was still a territory?

It was a painful decision, but he really had no choice. The frequency of his asthma attacks had increased. He was unable to work full time. There was a chance the change in climate might prove beneficial, but there was no guarantee. He had saved a little money — enough to tide them over for a few months. Mrs. Sexson and the children, Paul 4 and Edith 5, would remain in Indiana. If his condition improved, he would send for them.

The train trip on the Atchison, Topeka and Santa Fe took more than a week. Sexson had never seen a mountain or been a mile high. The hills of Yavapai were covered with pine trees and the little frontier town which served as a supply center for the miners and the cowboys was, he wrote his wife, "like a wild West novel come to life." He told her about the solid block of saloons on Montezuma Street across from the courthouse. He took a room at the Head Hotel on North Cortez; rent, $3.50 a week. His asthma was still troublesome. But since his arrival in Arizona, he felt better and he thought the climate was helping. He said he had looked around town and he might be able to get a job at the big general merchandise store of Bashford-Burmister. If not there, he would try Goldwater's.

To Daisy Sexson, reading her husband's letter in Indiana, Prescott seemed very far away. The street names — Montezuma and Cortez — appeared romantic. But if J. O. was better, if his asthma attacks were lessening in severity, nothing else mattered.

In his second letter he told his wife he had found a small shoe store that was for sale. His store in Gosport had a shoe department. He thought if his health continued to improve, he would try to buy this store and would soon be sending for the family.

Sexson did make a deal to buy the shoe store. He committed most of his savings to the down payment, signed the papers, and returned to the hotel to write his wife an optimistic letter. It was a small business, but he was sure the family could live on the income and he believed sales could be increased. Sometime before daylight his dream collapsed. He suffered a violent attack of asthma, which left him so weakened he had trouble getting out of bed. He knew he could not stay in Prescott. But he had signed the papers, made the first payment.

That afternoon Sexson went to see the owner of the shoe store. His daughter, Edith Sexson Brown Faville, does not remember the man's name, but she knows what happened. The owner was sympathetic and understanding. He tore up the agreement of sale and refunded the down payment her father had made. He said some folks suffering from asthma did better in the warm desert climate of Phoenix.

This experience had a profound effect on the young man from Indiana. He thought the change in climate had really worked wonders, only to have that midnight asthma attack destroy his hopes. Then he had thought the seller would surely claim all or part of the down payment; perhaps insist that Sexson carry out his part of the bargain. It was, he concluded, a demonstration of a difference in attitude between the settled East and the new frontier. He came to Phoenix, his health improved, and he spent most of the next 42 years of his life helping others enjoy the blessings of healthy minds and healthy bodies.

In a few weeks J. O. had a job selling shoes at H. A. Diehl's Store at 8 West Washington. In early January, 1912, he sent for his family, telling them he was confident the desert climate was gradually working the miracle they had all prayed for, that he was secure in his job at the shoe store, and had some wonderful new friends.

His daughter remembers the family arrived just a few days before Arizona was admitted to the Union. "We were staying at the Ford Hotel. On Admission Day, the new governor, George Hunt, walked all the way from the hotel to the state capitol at the other end of Washington Street. It was exciting. We joined the crowd and walked part of the way with him."

Edith remembers her father rented a small house in the capitol district. It was convenient because the Washington Street car line made it easy to travel downtown and to come to the First Methodist Church on Sundays.

Six feet tall, slender and well educated, J. O. Sexson was an outgoing, gregarious man. He made friends easily. He was enthusiastic about the future and, like many another newcomer, he was an ardent booster of his new home town.

At the Methodist Church he met Lloyd Christy, who was then cashier in the Valley Bank his father, Colonel William Christy, had started. He also met Dr. John Norton, H. B. Wilkinson, who was in the Legislature, and Kirby Samuel Townsend, the capitalist who later helped Lulu Clifton lease the building on Third Avenue for the Arizona Deaconess Hospital and Home.

In 1913, Sexson went to work as the collection teller in the Valley Bank of Phoenix. He bought some property on 19th Avenue, an old house with surrounding acreage, and became a part-time farmer. Daisy did not like the isolation. Sexson bought a Model T Ford. His daughter says the first time he brought it home he could not remember how to stop it and ran it through the back of the barn.

When the Valley Bank closed in November, 1914, Sexson lost his job. He bought a house at 338 North Fourth Avenue, farmed the country land, and worked at a number of part-time jobs.

Organized in 1892 by Colonel William Christy and Dr. J. C. Norton, the YMCA occupied an impressive two-story building on the north side of Monroe Street between First and Second Avenues. But the "Y" had outgrown its quarters. More space was needed. The directors decided to make a drive for capital funds. The man they asked to head this effort was J. O. Sexson.

The community was feeling the pinch of World War I. The farmers and cattlemen were hurting. But no one ever promised J. O. Sexson his life would be an easy one. He took the job with the title of Acting Secretary, raised the money, enlarged the building by adding another floor, and increased community participation — all this at a time of great personal tragedy.

Daisy Sexson, who had never been really ill a day in her life, whose strength had supported her husband in his struggle with asthma, developed serious symptoms.

A local doctor diagnosed the problem as appendicitis and wanted to operate. The only first class facilities in Phoenix were at St. Joseph's Hospital, and Daisy Sexson was the daughter of a Methodist minister. This may have influenced the decision to go back to Indiana, consult her old family doctor and secure a second opinion.

Sexson took his wife east. Her problem was not appendicitis, but diabetes. Insulin had not been discovered, and there was no treatment beyond diet. Daisy Sexson died in 1917.

J. O.'s sister, Hassie, came out from Indiana to take care of the children, 10-year-old Paul and 11-year-old Edith. The board of directors of the YMCA, more than satisfied with J. O.'s performance as acting secretary, made him general secretary of the "Y," and his sister got a job teaching math at Phoenix Union High School.

In 1917, Sexson helped organize and became a charter member of the first Kiwanis Club in Phoenix, an association which was to become an important supportive asset for his career.

It was through Kiwanis and the church that Sexson met Walter Wesley Knorpp and developed a friendship which endured for 36 years.

Wes Knorpp, whose contributions to his community would require a separate book the size of this one to chronicle, came to Phoenix on his own when he was 13 years old in 1905. In a remarkable personal memoir written to kick off the Phoenix Community Chest Drive 44 years later, Knorpp describes an event which happened soon after his arrival.

"A tall thin boy of 13 stood on Washington Street, facing south across the street from Korrick's. In the center stood the City Hall of Phoenix, surrounded by walks, grass and beautiful shade trees. The plaza occupied the full city block between First and Second Streets, Washington and Jefferson.

"A band, one of the early day extravagances of Phoenix, entertained a motley crowd of farmers, businessmen, Indians, Mexicans and Whites, from an ornate green and white bandstand.

"Colorful mendicants sold hot tamales, wonderfully good ones, to the crowd sitting around on the lawn.

"This sweltering Sunday afternoon the crowd was larger than usual because a rare treat was in store. After the concert we were going to hear about the future of Phoenix, and that is why I was there.

"Now let's take a look at the town in this year of 1905. Dust billowed up in clouds as a buggy drove by. Kids fought in the middle of the street. There wasn't one foot of paved street in this desert town of five thousand inhabitants. True, there were sidewalks and curbs on a few blocks of Washington and on Center Street. Saloons lined Washington Street from First Street to Center. Beautiful massive bars were 50 to 100 feet long, with the space opposite occupied by busy gambling tables and maybe a Chinese restaurant or eating counter to the rear.

"Vividly painted ladies of that day, wearing lovely sweeping dresses or very pretty, very short ones, plied their profession upstairs. A sad looking, loose jointed man of 25, who looked 70, would be pounding the ivories. The half-chewed cigar he held so viciously in his mouth was removed only to toss down another double jigger of rotgut. One famous place had a big painted sign displayed on the outside wall: 'We serve the worst whiskey in Arizona.'

"Some of the finest residences were just north of Van Buren on Center Street, but there weren't very many.

"When it rained the dust turned to slimy, slippery glue-like mud. By the time you crossed the street both feet looked like they were wearing gunnysacks. The adobe mud gathered gobs until you could fairly feel that on the very next step you might fail to extricate that foot.

"Now, let's get back to the plaza. The concert is over. There were several speakers. And now comes Mr. B. A. Fowler, early-day enthusiast, vigorous to a degree that belied the years he had attained. He shook his finger, he shook his fist, he shook his well-cut beard, and he spit out his determined words: 'We must be unflinching. We must fight. We must be optimistic. We must work together to accomplish our ends.'

" 'I predict,' said B. A. Fowler, 'that we shall build a great dam at Tonto. That we shall irrigate hundreds of thousands of acres. I predict there are those standing in this audience who shall see this entire Valley blossom like a rose. Rich crops will come forth. . .our Valley will have paved roads from the mountains on the north to the mountains on the south. Prosperous farmers, with electricity on every farm, will support a Phoenix beyond our most magnificent dreams'."

Wes was there in 1905 and he lived to see that prediction come true. He carried papers, delivered packages for Miller's Pharmacy, carried rural mail, was a bellhop, a night desk clerk at the Hotel Adams, and by 1909 he was the circulation manager of *The Arizona Republican.* He left that job to take a similar post with *The San Bernardino Free Press*; then moved to *The San Diego Tribune* to sell display advertising. Seven years later he was advertising manager at the *Tribune.*

In 1917, in response to a request from his long-time friend Charlie Stauffer, Wes Knorpp returned to Phoenix to take a job on *The Arizona Republican.* Twelve years later, after the death of pioneer publisher Dwight B. Heard, Knorpp and Stauffer acquired the newspaper. With the exception of two years in the armed forces in World War I, Wes Knorpp devoted his life to the papers and to the development of the commercial, cultural and civic institutions of his adopted city and state. Stauffer and Knorpp changed the name of the morning paper from *The Arizona Republican* to *The Arizona Republic.* They acquired the afternoon paper, *The Arizona Gazette*, and changed its name to *The Phoenix Gazette.* When radio was very new, the publishing company became a partner in the operation of the pioneer station KTAR.

The newspapers reflected the character of Knorpp and Stauffer. They believed in God and country. Knorpp was an active Methodist, and Stauffer a devout Episcopalian. They believed in public service. Stauffer, a member of the Phoenix City Council in territorial days, was a graduate of Tempe Normal School and an enthusiastic booster of that institution.

Under the leadership of Knorpp and Stauffer, the newspapers were almost non-partisan politically, but they were bold and persistent in the promotion of projects and institutions which could benefit the community.

In 1919, the YMCA was a flourishing concern. The building had been greatly improved, there was no outstanding debt, and J. O. Sexson enjoyed his work.

The affairs of the little Arizona Deaconess Hospital and Home were in sad shape. The building on McDowell had not been completed. There were uncollected pledges totaling more than $113,000. The hospital was operating in two locations — the old building on North Third Avenue and a small amount of usable space at 10th and McDowell. Neither facility was adequate. St. Joseph's was still the only first rate hospital in the Valley.

The hospital board of directors asked J. O. Sexson to come on their board and lead a drive for capital funds to finish the building on McDowell Road. The board members were all Sexson's good friends. He had worked with them in the Methodist Church, and they had worked with him for the YMCA. Sexson said yes.

The economy of the Salt River Valley was struggling to recover from the effects of World War I. Even if all those delinquent pledges were paid in full, there would not be enough money to complete the original project. But Sexson had been a remarkably successful fund raiser for the "Y." It would take time, he said, but it could be done. He would do it.

In 1920 the hospital board, confident the new building on McDowell would soon be completed, asked Miss Hazel Runyan, a registered nurse and an experienced hospital administrator, to come to Phoenix to take charge of the hospital as soon as the new building was occupied. Miss Runyan came, spent some time here, then decided to return to her former position in Ohio until the McDowell facilities were completed.

Methodist Hazel Runyan met Methodist J. O. Sexson at church. When she interviewed with the hospital board Sexson was there describing just how the fund drive would be conducted.

In 1921 Hazel Runyan came back to Phoenix, not to manage the new hospital because the building was still incomplete, but to marry J. O. Sexson.

In early June, 1922, Sexson, who had succeeded Wilkinson as president of the board of directors of the Arizona Deaconess Hospital and Home, announced the beginning of the long-awaited capital funds drive. He had spent almost two years laying the ground work. He personally solicited the support of all the banks, the Protestant churches, the board of the YMCA, the members of the Maricopa County Medical Society, and his good friend, Wes Knorpp of *The Arizona Republican*.

In the first two weeks of actual solicitation more than $50,000 was raised. When the drive was over, the total was more than $200,000.

K. S. Townsend was the largest single contributor. Among those giving more than $5,000 were Mr. and Mrs. Niels Petersen. Petersen, president of the Farmers and Merchants Bank of Tempe, had come to Arizona in 1871 and helped Jack Swilling dig his ditch. Petersen also served in the Territorial Legislature and, at one time, was a member of the Maricopa County Board of Supervisors. Mr. and Mrs. Dwight B. Heard gave $5,000. Mr. and Mrs. George H. Maxwell, who were then living in Boston, made a similar contribution. More than 40 service clubs and community organizations each contributed $1,000. Altogether, 3,500 individuals and organizations responded. One out of every six people living in the city made some gift, large or small. It was truly a remarkable accomplishment.

When the new hospital was dedicated on that Saturday afternoon of June, 1923, the talent and dedication of J. O. Sexson had made Lulu Clifton's dream a reality.

The completed building presented an imposing appearance. The main entrance was set back from McDowell Road 150 feet. In the architectural manner of the day, 16 steps took the visitor from the street level to what was the second floor and reception area of the hospital. Four magnificent columns, more than 40 feet high, defined this entrance. The columns were smooth, not fluted, topped with a cast capital, all in the tradition of great public buildings of that day. There was an ornate frieze in masonry relief above the columns and a masonry parapet above the frieze. A circular drive entered and exited on McDowell. The cornerstone, a block of granite about 30 inches high by 40 inches wide, had been put in place when construction first started. It says, "Arizona Deaconess Hospital. Erected 1918-19," and below that, "He healed them all."

CHAPTER 5

A New Home— A New Beginning

Newspaper reports of the opening of that new hospital building praised Sexson for his fund raising, emphasized that six Protestant churches had representatives on the hospital board, and took notice that board members Irvine, Dennett, Scott, Norton, Loper, Rogers, Christy, Coggins, and Miss Clifton had all been associated with the hospital for many years, and some of them were the original incorporators.

The reporter mentioned the excellent construction work performed by general contractor Clinton Campbell. In the advertising section, various subcontractors congratulated the hospital board. It was all a triumphant *fait accompli.* The struggle was over. The building was complete. The future assured. This was a day to celebrate.

Behind that facade of rosy optimism, the problems still confronting the board were obscured. It was not all that easy, as the minutes of the meetings preserved in the handwriting of secretary Rogers clearly reveal. On April 3, 1923, Coggins, recognizing there was not enough money on hand to complete and equip the new building, urged the appointment of a committee consisting of Sexson, Townsend, Rogers and Coggins to approach the banks and ask for an immediate emergency loan. Four days later, on April 7, the board, in special session at the YMCA, reviewed a letter from Sylvan Ganz, manager of the Phoenix Clearing House Association, stating that the Phoenix National Bank, the National Bank of Arizona and the Valley Bank would loan the board

$30,000 on a note to be signed personally by the members of the board.

All of the members had contributed generously to the capital fund drive but, two days later, on April 9, again in a special meeting at the YMCA, the board agreed to accept the loan and each member signed the documents acknowledging his personal liability. By today's standards, $30,000 is not much money. Divided by the 12 who signed, it was only $2,500 each. But, in 1923, $2,500 was a substantial obligation — a magnificent demonstration of the dedication these pioneers were willing to exhibit.

All of these special board meetings prior to the opening of the hospital were called to meet some new crisis. On June 8, Superintendent Mary J. Burns asked permission to hire a Miss Kettlewell to instruct the student nurses at a salary of $75.00 a month, and for authority to pay Miss Hackett, a surgical nurse, $100.00 a month. Deaconess Emma Wolfe, a dietitian and close friend of Lulu Clifton, had been discharged for failing to maintain discipline in the kitchen. The matter of her severance had to be settled.

On June 23, 1923, the board held its first meeting in the dining room of the new hospital. Sexson, who had led the successful fund drive, was president; Townsend, vice-president; Irvine, treasurer; and Scott, auditor. The Methodist Church was represented by three clergymen, S. J. Rogers, Bishop A. W. Leonard and the Reverend J. A. Stavely. The other board members were Coggins, Loper, Goodman, Cox, who had taken the place of his law partner, Judge Phillips, Lulu Clifton, Christy, Aldrich, Dennett and Norton.

Doctor N. E. Davis of Chicago, secretary at the Board of Hospitals and Homes for the Methodist Church, outlined requirements for operating a standardized hospital.

The old ways of doing things must be abandoned. Every doctor eligible to membership in the County Medical Association would be entitled to practice in the new building. The board must appoint a staff and a notice must be sent to every medical doctor informing him of the privilege. The medical staff must select its own chief and be responsible for the medical administration. Dr. Davis suggested the staff should be divided into medical, surgical and diagnostic committees.

The board, in consultation with the superintendent, must establish salary scales and control working conditions. A policy must be adopted as to how much charity or free medical service the hospital would provide. The board would establish room rates and charges for use of the operating rooms, X-ray, obstetrical equipment, etc. At the converted residence on West Taylor and the 15-bed institution on Third Avenue, operational problems and policies had been settled by the superintendent. Now all that had to be changed. And, of course,there was the ever present need for additional capital funding.

Three weeks and one day after the new building was opened, the board met in an emergency session to approve the acceptance of a loan of $50,000 from the Pacific Mutual Life Insurance Company of California, arranged by H. B. Wilkinson of the Phoenix Title and Trust. The loan would be secured by a first mortgage on the new property on McDowell. The minutes reflect that Phoenix Title handled the transaction, prepared the necessary legal papers, and recorded the mortgage — all without charge to the hospital.

It was obvious, almost from the start, that the task of operating the hospital in the new building would be too great for one person. Janet Burns was a very competent supervisor of the day-to-day activities, but a business manager was needed to handle the fiscal affairs. J. A. Bowman was hired to serve in this capacity.

J. O. Sexson was still earning his living as general secretary of the YMCA, but his volunteer duty as chairman of the board of directors of the hospital claimed an increasing amount of his attention. The "Y" was a convenient meeting place for the board, and it saved J. O. travel time. A great many of the board meetings between the opening of the hospital and the fall of 1924 were held in the Secretary's office at the "Y".

At one meeting, the matter of cleaning up and landscaping the hospital grounds was discussed. K. S. Townsend and Dr. Norton each offered to provide a team of horses to be used for the work, without charge, provided the hospital would feed them and employ a man to use them.

On October 10, 1923, the Methodist minister, Dr. S. J. Rogers, who had served as financial secretary of the hospital for so many years, was transferred to California. This meant an additional burden for the board president. Edith Sexson Faville says that during these years when her dad wore two hats, his family saw very little of him.

"My stepmother was a wonderful person. She gave us love and understanding and support. She also was Dad's strong right arm, because she knew so much about what hospitals should or should not do. Dad spent more time working on the problems of the hospital than he did on the 'Y,' but the 'Y' was in good shape, and most of the members of the 'Y' board also served on the hospital board. They did not complain. By the time I was ready to enroll at the University of Redlands in 1924, we all knew Dad could not continue being responsible for both the 'Y' and the hospital."

On October 27, 1924, K. S. Townsend, vice-president of the board of directors of the Arizona Deaconess Hospital and Home, and L. W. Coggins, president of the board of directors for the YMCA, made a joint announcement. J. O. Sexson resigned as secretary of the "Y" and had accepted appointment as business manager of Deaconess Hospital. His wife Hazel, former superintendent of the Flower Hospital in Toledo, Ohio, would become superintendent.

Sexson expressed some regret over leaving his post at the "Y". *The Arizona Republican* reported that during the eight years J. O. had served as general secretary of that organization membership had grown from a little over 500 to 1,175. The heavy mortgage on the building had been paid off and the affairs of the "Y" were in great shape.

The paper did not say so, but the Deaconess Hospital was still struggling. J. A. Bowman had resigned; Janet Burns had asked to be relieved as superintendent. For the rest of his life, J. O. devoted his considerable talents to the management and expansion of the hospital.

K. S. Townsend was named president of the hospital board, and Nelson W. Benning became the new secretary of the "Y". The change in leadership did not diminish the close association between the "Y" and the hospital, and some time later hospital administrator Sexson became president of the board of directors of the "Y".

Sexson persuaded his good friend and fellow Kiwanian, Wes Knorpp, to become a member of the hospital board. These volunteers did not take their responsibilities lightly. Knorpp served 45 years before resigning in 1968. It is truly remarkable that so many of the board members served from the day of their first appointment almost to the day of their death, and most of them attended every meeting. Perhaps the community in those days was more settled, but a better explanation is to be found in the fact that it was a working body. The board made all of the big decisions when problems confronted the hospital. And those chosen to serve on the board were established community leaders.

It could not have been the salary offered which persuaded Sexson to take the job. In 1924, the business manager and the superintendent together were paid a total of $620.75 a month. Hospital income in April of that year was $8,888.70 and expenses $7,154.82. There was less than $500.00 in the capital fund account.

As the leader of that first successful fund drive, Sexson had persuaded the board to abandon its strictly parochial Methodist sponsorship and reach out to other communions. As administrator he continued his efforts. The constitution and by-laws were amended to remove some restrictive clauses.

In 1926 the board first considered changing the name of the hospital, but no action was taken. The minutes of the meeting for March 27 of that year record that Miss Lulu Clifton was seriously ill and a patient in the hospital. The board instructed business manager Sexson to purchase some flowers for the deaconess. And the board authorized Sexson to enter into a contract with the federal government to provide medical care for veterans of World War I. The hospital submitted a bid to the Shrine to care for 20 crippled children at a rate of $2.85 per day.

Brill Street was paved and the hospital was charged $2,163 as its share of the cost. There was a threat of a malpractice suit and the directors agreed to employ the firm of Kibbey, Bennett, Gust and Smith to defend against the claim, if the attorneys and the lawyers for the insurance company felt such a move would be beneficial.

In December of 1926, the hospital had to borrow $5,000 from the Valley Bank to meet the payments on the mortgage owed to Pacific Mutual and to the Utleys, whose spacious home at 1105 East McDowell Road had been purchased by the hospital in 1924 as a residence for the business manager and superintendent. In 1927, board member J. A. R. Irvine died. Guy Alsap and Judge Frank O. Smith were named to the board.

Alsap was a native Phoenician. His father, Doctor John T. Alsap, came to Arizona from California in 1864 and was probably the first doctor to settle in what became Phoenix. But he did not practice medicine; he practiced law. He was appointed Treasurer of the Arizona Territory under President Cleveland, was the first mayor of Phoenix, and the first probate judge of Maricopa county.

Guy Alsap and his brother, John W., owned and operated the Donofrio Confectionery Company.

Judge Smith was a partner in the law firm of Kibbey, Bennett, Gust and Smith. Kibbey had drafted the articles of incorporation for the Salt River Valley Water Users' Association and served as governor of Arizona from 1905 to 1909.

John Gust, who came to Phoenix in 1909, had first practiced with the firm headed by Louis Chalmers, and Mrs. Chalmers had been chairman of the first Deaconess Hospital building committee.

J. O. Sexson may not have been an expert in hospital administration when he accepted the appointment as business manager of the "Deaconess," but he did understand the importance of involving as many community leaders as possible to support the hospital by naming them to the board of trustees.

In 1928 Moses B. Hazeltine, of Prescott, dean of the State's banking community, joined the board, as did Mrs. John C. Greenway, whose husband had developed the copper prospects at Ajo. In 1933, Mrs. Greenway was elected to Congress when Congressman Lewis W. Douglas resigned to join the Roosevelt administration. She was reelected in 1934. Indiana capitalist T. C. McReynolds; Dr. A. J. Chandler, southside real estate developer for whom the town of Chandler is named; H. J. McClung, president of the Phoenix National Bank; George Mickle; and D. J. Peters became board members. Mickle, who came to Arizona in 1913 from Ohio, along with D. J. Peters, organized the Pay'N-Takit chain of grocery stores which served all of Arizona. In 1927 the stores were sold to the Safeway system. Mickle then joined Thomas Clements in purchasing control of the Phoenix Title and Trust Company. Mickle served on the hospital board until 1944. Two members from the Valley's agricultural community joined the board at Sexson's request: C. H. McKellips, the area's leading citrus grower, and produce farmer Floyd O. Smith.

By 1928 the need for funds to pay off indebtedness and expand the hospital had reached a point where a decision must be made. The board decided to issue bonds, to the amount of $125,000, bearing an interest rate not to exceed six percent. Sexson reported that George Hebard Maxwell, who was living in Los Angeles at the time, had agreed to subscribe to one-half of all the bonds issued, provided the hospital would change its name from "Deaconess" to "Good Samaritan."

ANGENY BUILDING
On North Third Avenue, occupied by the Arizona Deaconess Hospital from 1915 to 1923.

DR. FERDINAND ANGENY
Pioneer physician who opened the second hospital to be established in Phoenix at 215 North Third Avenue. The building was later rented to the Arizona Deaconess Hospital.

H. B. WILKINSON
—Photograph from the Historical Collection of Herb and Dorothy McLaughlin

LLOYD B. CHRISTY
Mayor of Phoenix, original incorporator of the Deaconess Hospital.
—from The Arizona Museum Collection

LULU CLIFTON
Methodist Deaconess who came to Arizona to die with tuberculosis and lived to organize the Arizona Deaconess Hospital.

COL. L. W. COGGINS
Pioneer businessman and civic leader, mayor
of Phoenix and a member of the board of trustees of the Deaconess-Samaritan hospital from
1918-1953.

DR. CHARLES B. PALMER

REVEREND HARDY A. INGHAM

COL WILLIAM CHRISTY
Farmer, banker, who suggested the method of
financing which has permitted the construction
of reclamation projects in the West.
—from The Arizona Museum Collection

GEORGE HEBARD MAXWELL
An evangelist of reclamation, he persuaded the Arizona Deaconess to change the name of their hospital to Good Samaritan.
—Stephen Shadegg

DWIGHT B. HEARD
Owner and publisher of *The Arizona Republican.* His family gave the land at Central and McDowell now occupied by the Library, Art Center and Little Theatre.

VERNON L. CLARK
Leader in the drive to convince land owners to mortgage their property and construct Roosevelt Dam.
—Stephen Shadegg

GENERAL MOSES HAZELTINE SHERMAN
Teacher, entrepreneur, politician. Responsible for the relocation of the territorial capital from Prescott to Phoenix.

ORIGINAL ST. JOSEPH'S HOSPITAL
Founding Sisters on porch.

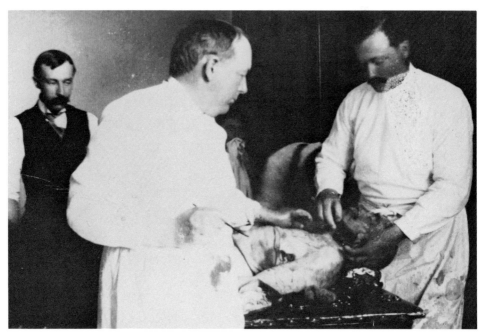

OPERATION - ST. JOSEPH'S HOSPITAL
April 1, 1897, Dr. Henry Hughes in the foreground.
            —John Hughes

DEDICATION OF ROOSEVELT DAM
March 18, 1911.
                    —Stephen Shadegg

DR. HENRY A. HUGHES
Commenced practice in Phoenix in 1886, helped organize the Arizona Medical Association. Father of Dr. Coit I. Hughes.
—John Hughes

DR. COIT I. HUGHES
Son of the pioneer surgeon, Henry A. Hughes, commenced practice in Arizona in 1901.
—John Hughes

DR. WILLIAM ELLIS
First chief of staff named when the Deaconess Hospital moved to the new building on McDowell Road.

DR. WIN WYLIE
Pioneer physician who was also qualified in law but chose to practice the healing arts.

DR. J. C. NORTON
One-time State Veterinarian, first Recording Secretary of the YMCA, long-time member of the board of trustees, Good Samaritan Hospital.

B. A. FOWLER
Who helped organize and served as first president of the Salt River Valley Water Users' Association.
—Stephen Shadegg

MOSES HAZELTINE
Dean of the pioneer banking community and a faithful member of the board of trustees of the Good Samaritan Hospital.

JOHN P. ORME
First elected president of the Salt River Valley Water Users' Association.
—Stephen Shadegg

Earlier, the words "and Home" had been dropped without objection from the official bodies of the Methodist Church. This time there was no protest over the change in name from "Deaconess" to "Good Samaritan." Officially, and unofficially, the Methodist Deaconess Association and the Board of Hospitals and Homes of the Methodist Episcopal Church supported and approved the services provided for the community by the hospital. But the financial burden, which had always been considerable, had increased.

The articles of incorporation and the bylaws of the hospital were changed to reflect the new name, permit the enlargement of the board, and remove the requirements that the majority of the board memberships must be filled by Methodist churchmen. But the Methodist Conference insisted on the retention of the reverter clause which had been included in the original gift of the land on McDowell Road to the hospital.

Under the terms of this clause, if the land is ever used for anything other than hospital purposes — non-profit — title to the land and all buildings, improvements and equipment must revert to the Methodist Conference.

In 1928, when the board approved the issuance of $125,000 worth of interest-bearing bonds, the hospital was $112,716 in debt and urgently needed $12,000 for new equipment and refurbishing. As security for the bonds, the hospital pledged a trust deed, or mortgage, on the real property of the corporation, consisting of all of Block 16 of Brill Addition of the City of Phoenix, buildings, improvements, and equipment located thereon.

In April, 1928, the original articles of incorporation were substantially amended by a vote of the members, and the name of the institution became officially Good Samaritan Hospital.

Despite the indifferent success of the capital funds drive, and the inability of the hospital to market the $125,000 in bonds (Maxwell was unable to meet his commitment), plans proceeded to build an additional wing. Eventually, the money, $250,000, was provided by the Real Estate Mercantile and Trust Company of St. Louis, underwriters for the bond issue. Contractor William Pepper was the successful bidder on plans provided by Royal Lescher of the firm of Lescher and Mahoney, Architects, and construction was commenced.

The Great Depression of 1929 was late in coming to Arizona. However, when the full force and effect of that financial catastrophe was felt, every segment of the economy suffered, and the difficulty of keeping Good Samaritan Hospital afloat increased.

The monthly meetings of the board of directors were devoted entirely to plugging holes in the hospital's financial ship. When the Methodist Conference was unable, or unwilling, to advance $75,000, J. O. Sexson went to Salt Lake City and, with the assistance of leaders of the Arizona Mormon community, he was able to persuade the Church of Jesus Christ of Latter Day Saints to advance the needed funds. Steve Morris, who came to Good Samaritan as an administrative assistant many years later, delights in repeating what Sexson told him about that trip to Salt Lake City. "I went up there to ask for a loan. The elders said they would not make the loan, but they would give us the money to carry on the work we were doing."

For Lulu Clifton, who faithfully attended the meetings of the board of directors, the hospital's financial problems were especially painful. But she never lost faith in the ultimate destiny — the mission — of the organization she had started. Her entire life had been one of triumph and disaster. She had been graduated from the Deaconess School at the top of her class, earned the approval of her superiors in the organization, and had her life so well planned, when illness forced her to cancel her engagement to the Reverend Edmund Bristow and come west to the wild Territory of Arizona.

After numerous setbacks, her dream of a hospital had been fulfilled in that June of 1923. Two years later, the Reverend Mr. Bristow, now a widower, reappeared in Miss Lulu's life. He came to visit Miss Clifton and her mother at the house on North 12th Avenue. No longer in the active ministry, he was occupied with writing poetry and sermons, lecturing and teaching. Within a year he was writing Miss Clifton eloquent letters of love and beseeching her to marry him.

It may have been that Lulu Clifton's strong sense of obligation to her elderly mother prevented her from accepting Mr. Bristow's offer. It may have been her feelings had changed and she could not rekindle the fire. In his letters Bristow charges that the hospital had become her main interest in life, that she feared marriage might interfere. At any rate, she told Mr. Bristow no. He would not take no for an answer. He kept writing her, kept insisting.

Mrs. Al Morley, who has lived at the address on North 12th Avenue since 1937, first as a tenant renting from Miss Clifton and then as owner after the deaconess' death in 1959, remembers Miss Clifton talking about this middle age romance. When Miss Lulu died, the love letters written by Edmund Bristow came into Mrs. Morley's possession.

Whatever her reasons for refusing marriage, it was a very painful time for Miss Lulu. In his disappointment, Bristow changed from pleading lover to bitter critic. He sent vile letters, condemning Lulu's mother and Lulu for her devotion to her mother. He even threatened to sue for breach of promise. Through it all, Miss Clifton kept up her work and life of service. Mrs. Morley remembers walking with the deaconess to WCTU meetings, which often ended late at night, and of going to the city jail with her to comfort the prisoners.

"She was living alone by the time we moved here, but she was never alone. There was always someone who needed help. The B. J. Jarretts, who lived on West Monroe, were her good friends. Del E. Webb, who was a beginning contractor, constructed the home Lulu was living in when she died — a two-story building erected at the rear of the original lot on North 12th Avenue. Miss Emma Wolfe, Lulu's friend who had been a dietitian at the hospital, rented the downstairs apartment."

Mrs. Morley says Lulu Clifton never gave up. She was never discouraged, never despondent. She loved the Lord and reflected the love of the Lord on everyone she met.

CHAPTER 6

School of Nursing

Lulu Clifton and those community leaders who joined her in organizing the Arizona Deaconess Hospital intended to create a teaching institution. The second paragraph of the original articles itemizing their purpose says, "To establish, maintain and conduct a school for the proper training of Christian women as nurses." There was no place for this in the temporary quarters on West Taylor Street, but after the move to the Angeny Building the board of trustees took steps to implement that second purpose.

On September 1, 1922, Miss Katrina Olsen graduated from the "training school" operated by the Deaconess Hospital as a diplomaed nurse and was certified by the state board as a registered nurse. The meager records existing show she was graded on punctuality, interest, obedience, attention, memory, neatness, and reliability. The only grades noted for actual class work were in Bacteriology, 99, and Obstetrics, 87.

It has been said that student nurses in those days were trained to make beds, empty bedpans, and not much else. According to her time sheets, Miss Olsen worked 282 hours a month, spent six hours each week studying general nursing, and seven hours on materia medica. She was on duty 12 hours a day, seven days a week, and was paid $5.00 per month plus room and board.

In the next 53 years the Deaconess Hospital, and its successor Good Samaritan, maintained an on-premises nursing school and graduated 1,400 qualified registered nurses.

Gertrude Wallace Hill, in a remarkable first person statement preserved in the archives, provides a vivid description of those early days.

In 1920, Miss Wallace, whose home was in Phoenix, went to Kansas City, Missouri, where she enrolled in a hospital nursing school. She says, "I had been in training in Kansas City, Missouri, for a year when I was sent home to Phoenix because of my illness. When I was well enough to work, I answered an advertisement for a stenographer for Mary Janet Burns, R.N., who was the administrator and superintendent of nurses at the Arizona Deaconess Hospital. I got the position and went to work in mid-summer of 1922.

"Miss Burns was the head. Elizabeth Blakemen, R.N., was a surgical supervisor, and also a substitute for Miss Burns when she was absent from the hospital. Emma Wolfe was dietitian and cook. These women comprised the top personnel and were all deaconesses of the Methodist Church.

"There were seven or eight nursing students, to the best of my recollection, which was ample for the size of the hospital — it being not more than 20 beds."

Miss Wallace recalls that the physical arrangements of the building on North Third Avenue indicated it was built as a hospital many years before, though she said it had the appearance of a large residence with three floors.

"These student nurses were Katrina and Ragna Olsen, Lucille Yaeger, May Day, Ora Davidson, Thina Wilson, Minnie Hess, Geneva Provence. There was also a janitor, who at times helped out as the orderly."

Ragna Olsen, Thina Wilson, and Lucille Yaeger earned their diplomas and certification in 1923; Minnie Hess and Geneva Provence in 1924.

"Miss Burns and Miss Blakemen had come to the Arizona Deaconess Hospital from the Methodist Deaconess Hospital in Bozeman, Montana. It was their plan to work, with the help of a board of deaconesses headed by Lulu Clifton as president, to complete the new hospital on McDowell Road.

"I cannot recall when the present Good Samaritan Hospital was started. I do recall, however, it was years previous to my leaving Phoenix in 1921 to enter nurse's training that the steel framework of the West Wing and the front of the hospital, that included only the pillars, stood as a memorial to the efforts of the

Methodist deaconesses who could not go ahead with its completion due to financial embarrassment. This fact all came out during my stenographic work for Miss Burns and for the board. An interesting note regarding the site of the new hospital in '22 was that it was located 'out in the country' where it would be nice and quiet for the patients.

"Salaries at that time were low as compared to now. For instance, I received $30.00 per month, plus my maintenance. The students received a small fee, $5.00 per month. The students lived on the third floor of the hospital and were as comfortable as the rest of us. There was no such thing as refrigeration or air conditioning. It got pretty hot in the summer months and, by the same token, pretty cold in the winter months. I was about the same age as the students and went with them to movies, to the 'YW' where we swam, and very occasionally to Riverside Park where we danced. This latter diversion was frowned on by the deaconesses. On the lot north of the building were trees and benches where students sometimes entertained their boyfriends.

"I lived with the 'top personnel' and that was in a boarded up tent. That is, the walls were boards for six feet high from the floor and the rest was canvas. This tent extended north and south and was located to the back of the lot next to the hospital on the north. It was accessible from the back door of the hospital, a distance of ten to 12 yards. We had comfortable single beds. Each had a dresser and a wardrobe to hang our clothing. It was a dormitory affair, though Miss Burns had screens for curtains around her corner. There was a potbellied stove that heated the tent during cold and inclement weather. During such times, before we arose in the morning, the janitor came in and started the fire. I can't recall being uncomfortable or inconvenienced in our way of living, except for bathing. The only thing we had was a small lean-to at the back of the tent, which served as a shower but it only had cold water. After becoming used to it, it served its purpose.

"The kitchen was the last room on the north side of the hospital. It was small, possibly ten or 12 feet square. The north and west walls were open and screened from six feet up, similar to the tent we lived in, and had canvas flaps on frames that could enclose it completely in bad weather. The dining room was another tent affair a few steps apart from the hospital's back door. The food served to all of us at one long table was home cooked and delicious. The patients were served first, of the same food that we had.

They had hand bells to ring to call a nurse and, if during a meal a bell rang, one of the students would answer it. This dining room also served as a classroom. Doctors lectured here and Miss Burns and Miss Blakemen taught all subjects required from practically the same type of books I had used in my year of training in Kansas City.

"My duties were to take dictation from Miss Burns and transcribe her letters, type up the questions for tests for the students, write up the minutes of the board meetings, and, finally, I was also typing the physicals and histories of the patients. The hospital was full most of the time and the patients, as far as I was able to determine from my year of training in a hospital of 250 beds, got excellent care.

"Some of the doctors on the staff that I recall to mind were Charles Vivian, E. Payne Palmer, C. B. Palmer (no relation to E. P.), Elton R. Charvoz, Arthur J. MacIntyre, Stillman D. Little, and Spencer D. Whiting. Quite a lot of surgery was done. Two medical cases I vividly recall were typhoid and anthrax. I do not recall too much about obstetrics, though. On the second floor was the nursery with four or five cribs.

"Work on the new building was going ahead by late fall of '22, and in '23 the cornerstone was laid. In the metal box which was placed in the cornerstone — if it is ever opened — will be found a Kodak snap of me, another snapshot of the group of students, documents, and, who knows, maybe a more complete history of the Methodist deaconesses and the Arizona Deaconess Hospital.

"I resigned my position with Miss Burns and returned to the hospital in Kansas City to complete training in September, 1923. I graduated two years later and returned to Phoenix in January of '26, where I did private duty at the Good Samaritan Hospital. In the meantime, Miss Blakemen had returned to Montana, Miss Burns had passed away, and Mrs. Sexson was the director of nurses. Miss Emma Wolfe was still the dietitian at the new hospital."

The Deaconess School of Nursing was accredited by the Arizona State Board of Nursing Examiners in 1922. If by modern standards the curriculum appears to be limited, it apparently more than satisfied the nursing requirements of that time.

When the move was made from North Third Avenue to McDowell Road in 1923, hospital board member K. S. Townsend personally financed the construction of a frame building which was used as classrooms and housing for the students.

In 1925 the hospital purchased the Utley house, a substantial two-story residence at 11th Street and McDowell. The Sexsons occupied the first floor. The second floor and the basement housed the student nurses; that year there were only two graduates. The frame structure K. S. Townsend had constructed was turned into a tubercular ward.

When the name of the hospital was officially changed to Good Samaritan in April, 1928, the name of the training school was changed to the Good Samaritan Hospital School of Nursing. That year the school graduated 11 trained nurses. There were 19 in the graduating class of 1929, but the effects of the Great Stock Market Crash and the nationwide Depression brought a reduction in student enrollment, and for the next several years it was touch and go for the hospital and for the School of Nursing.

In the relatively prosperous year of 1928, Sexson had successfully raised $120,000 by public subscription and borrowed $125,000 from the Phoenix Title and Trust Company to finance the construction of an additional wing at an estimated cost of about $300,000. The new East Wing was formally opened January 25, 1931. By 1932, the hospital improvements and grounds were appraised at over $800,000 — but the corporate debt was $282,000.

In those years from 1931 to 1935 the hospital was constantly in debt to the Valley National Bank for funds to pay running expenses. Between 1931 and 1935 the number of patients being served actually decreased.

In 1932 the population in Phoenix was less than 50,000 and there were fewer than 50 doctors in active practice. But more than 20 maintained offices in the Grunow Clinic at the corner of McDowell and Ninth Street, a handsome new building funded by William C. Grunow and his wife Valborg. In 1930 the Grunows' seven-year-old daughter Lois had died and the parents believed a lack of adequate clinical facilities in Phoenix was responsible. The rest of the medical men were officed in the Professional Building at Central and Monroe (which had excellent refrigerated air conditioning), the Goodrich Building at the corner of Central and Washington, the Ellis Building erected by Dr. W. C. Ellis at the corner of Second Avenue and Monroe, the Physicians' Building at

125 West Monroe, and a few in the Heard Building on North Central.

In those beginning years, while the hospital was struggling with its financial problems, Mrs. J. O. (Hazel) Sexson, who served as superintendent of the nursing training school from 1924 to 1935, was constantly upgrading the curriculum. Edith Sexson Brown Faville says her stepmother was a strict disciplinarian.

"Most of the students were afraid of her, but they all seemed to appreciate the quality of instruction they were receiving. And, while they may have chafed under the rigid rules of conduct imposed by the board of trustees and the long hours they had to put in at the hospital in addition to their studies, Nurses Home was a happy place."

In 1932 the Sexsons built a new home in an orange grove on North 16th Street, and the student nurses took over all three floors of the Utley residence.

"In 1937, the board of trustees published four pages of *Regulations Governing Student Nurses.*

"Those seeking admittance had to be high school graduates with at least sixteen credits.

"Chemistry was the one required subject.

"Students were required to provide their own uniforms.

"The school would not accept married women for training.

"The student could have one late leave and stay out to 11:00 p.m. once a week.

"They were expected to attend morning prayers and regular weekly chapel services, and were encouraged to attend services in their regular church as often as possible.

"They had to provide their own notebooks and fountain pens meeting regulations specified by the hospital.

"They could not receive telephone calls during hours on duty.

"They were not to carry on prolonged conversations on the telephone, as hospital lines are too busy for extended visiting.

"The use of the drugstore phone was forbidden.

"Their rooms were inspected regularly for neatness and cleanliness.

"They could not appear in the living room in negligees.

"The length of the uniform was to be ten inches above the floor. Brassieres were to be worn by all nurses.

"It was compulsory that every nurse have breakfast before going on duty. Eating on wards was not permitted.

"Students were forbidden to smoke while in the school.

"Borrowing and lending among students was discouraged.

"Students were not permitted to accept gratuities from patients.

"Swimming, desert parties and similar functions had to be properly chaperoned.

"Students were required to take care of their personal laundry during the week, as use of the irons and boards was prohibited on Sunday."

By 1940 first semester students were spending six hours of each week in classes on anatomy and physiology, three hours on microbiology, two hours on history of nursing, two hours of professional adjustment, two hours on pharmacology and therapeutics, one hour in pathology, three hours in nutrition, eight hours in fundamental nursing arts—a total of 27 hours of instruction each week.

In 1944 the student nurse worked in the hospital on a 12-hour shift six and one-half days each week and, before graduation, spent 1,019 hours in classroom instruction. About 25 highly qualified faculty members—most of them practicing physicians on the hospital staff—gave the instruction: Joseph Bank, Gastroenterology; Preston Brown, Gynecology; Palmer Dysart, Surgery; Joseph Madison Greer, Orthopedics; Norman Hall, Surgery; Hillary Ketcherside, Urology; Henry Running, Pediatrics; Lloyd Swasey, Internal Medicine; Clarence Warrenburg, Obstetrics; Henry Williams, Surgery; Clare Barth, a graduate of the Posse Nessen School of Boston, Physiotherapy; Faith Dravis, Medical Technologies.

In 1946 a new building to house the student nurses was constructed on McDowell Road east of the hospital, at a cost of more than $350,000, and named Sexson Hall in honor of J. O. and Hazel Sexson. In 1954, this building was enlarged to provide space for a total student body of 175.

Throughout the nation the training of nurses was generally regarded as a hospital responsibility. There were approximately 1,250 hospital-sponsored schools of nursing qualified to grant diplomas.

Nursing was an honorable but not highly paid profession, the nursing schools offered an educational opportunity to those who could not afford to enter college. Students received free room and board, a modest stipend, and paid no tuition. It has been suggested that some girls chose to enter nurses training because they hoped to marry doctors. True or not, proximity worked its magic and a very high percentage of doctors' wives were nurses before their marriage.

As early as 1928 the need to upgrade the curriculum in the nation's schools of nursing was widely recognized. Pioneers in this field urged the establishment of baccalaureate programs in established universities, with the granting of a bachelor of science degree in Nursing to those students who successfully completed the prescribed courses. The Arizona State Nurses Association strongly supported these proposals, but little was done.

In 1943 Miss Vivian Biggers, Director of Nurses at the Good Samaritan Hospital and in charge of the School of Nursing, sent a letter to Dr. George Bateman, professor of Chemistry at Arizona State Teachers College in Tempe, urging the establishment of a baccalaureate program in Nursing Science at the college.

As a result of the Biggers letter, President Grady Gammage appointed a committee to study the possibility and in the 1944–45 catalogue a number of programs were offered. Students could earn academic credit at the Teachers College (one or two years) and a diploma from an accredited nursing school. Graduates from accredited nursing schools would be given 16 hours of credit by the academic institution. But under this combination plan a student pursuing a degree was required to spend at least five, and oftentimes six, years in school.

The rapid advancement in medical science, the introduction of antibiotics, and the development of sophisticated technical instruments and apparatus for diagnosis and treatment clearly dictated the need for improvements in both medical and nursing education. But inertia, jealousies and lack of funds made the process painfully slow.

In 1945 the name of the school in Tempe was changed from "Arizona State Teachers College" to "Arizona State College," permitting the granting of degrees in disciplines other than Education. In that year there were only 933 students. Even so, Arizona, thanks to the foresight of President Grady Gammage and the pressure from the director of nursing at Good Samaritan Hospital, was pioneering the new approach and setting a pattern for other states to follow. There were, however, a number of obvious drawbacks. Not all of the young ladies desirous of becoming nurses could afford to finance one or two academic years at Tempe, and there was a recognized need to upgrade the clinical training offered by the diploma schools.

Commencing in 1948 all students enrolled in the Good Samaritan program were required to take some Arizona State College extension courses. The hospital paid the tuition costs and the students were enrolled at ASC so that a transcript was available. This was not the universal practice throughout the country, and some students who received extension instruction were not officially enrolled and had to repeat the courses to gain academic credit.

Vurlyne Boan, R.N., who came to the Good Samaritan school as an instructor in 1951 and was made director in 1965 (a post she held until the school was officially closed in 1973), makes some interesting comments on the development of faculty and curriculum.

Mrs. Boan says, "In 1951 there were three full-time faculty members. By the middle '60s there were 25 on the resident faculty and more than 180 full time students." During this period the curriculum was constantly upgraded and instructors at the school were required to meet higher educational qualifications.

General awareness of the problem was heightened, particularly in Arizona, when the hospitals began to experience difficulty in recruiting an adequate number of nurses. Pay scales were higher in California, and diploma schools in Arizona could not meet the demand, and nurses recruited from out of state frequently moved on to "greener pastures" after their first encounter with Arizona's summertime temperatures.

In 1951 President Gammage appointed a committee to study the development of a four-year degreed program in Nursing Education at Arizona State College. On that committee were a number of laypersons with vast experience in the health provider field. They were Miss Freida Erhardt, executive secretary of the Arizona State Board of Nurses Examiners and Nursing Education and president of the Arizona State Nurses Association; Dr. Joseph Kappa, president of the Arizona Hospital Association; Mrs. Marjorie Kasun, chairman of the Committee for the Improvement of Nursing Education; and Guy M. Hanner, administrator of Good Samaritan Hospital. This committee's report, made public in 1952, recommended the establishment of a collegiate school of nursing under the administrative direction of a dean at ASC.

In these early efforts emphasis was placed on the need for improving the quality of education of student nurses. In 1954 *Arizona Medicine* published a report stating "the cost of training student nurses at most of the nursing schools is $1,400 per student per year." The report said this was "a net cost, figured after the value of the services which the nurse renders to school or hospital has been taken into consideration." What these figures meant was that patients in the hospitals were paying for the cost of training student nurses.

In 1955 Guy M. Hanner, secretary/treasurer of the Arizona Hospital Association, informed President Gammage that the hospital administrators had adopted a resolution urging the establishment of a collegiate school of nursing at Tucson, or Tempe, or both.

A copy of this resolution was sent to the Board of Regents and to Ernest McFarland, Governor of Arizona. A committee was appointed by Arizona State College to draft a tentative program for such a school in August of 1956. The members were Dr. Arnold Tilden, dean of the College of Liberal Arts, chairman; Dr. Jesse Rannells, chairman and professor of Nutrition; Dr. George Bateman, professor of Chemistry; Dr. Herbert Stahnke, professor of Biological Sciences; Loretta Anderson, Director of Nursing, Good Samaritan Hospital; and Vurlyne Boan, Assistant Director of Nursing at Good Samaritan.

Dr. Norman Ross, a respected physician and surgeon who was on the staff at both Good Samaritan and St. Joseph's, explained to Miss Anderson the question was "where," not "if." Ross, who was a close friend of Governor McFarland's and active in Democratic Party politics, said the Board of Regents would be pressured by partisan supports of the University of Arizona not to authorize the baccalaureate program at Tempe. His solution was simple: Ask the Board of Regents to authorize the program at all three state schools. On October 3, 1956, the Board of Regents passed an official resolution authorizing the establishment of baccalaureate programs leading to a B.S. degree in Nursing Science at the University of Arizona, Arizona State College and the institution located in Flagstaff.

Loretta Anderson Hanner Bardewyck, author of an authoritative history on the development of the baccalaureate nursing program in Arizona and the first dean of the Nursing College at ASC (ASU), credits Good Samaritan Hospital, the School of

Nursing, Administrator Guy Hanner, and the hospital board of directors with playing major roles in the events which led up to the establishment of the new college at Tempe. The records support her claim.

In 1953, Loretta Anderson came to Good Samaritan as an assistant to Mrs. Josephine Steiner, Director of Nursing. Miss Anderson was a diplomaed graduate of Michael Reese Hospital in Chicago. She had earned her B.S. degree from the University of Minnesota and a M.S. degree from Cornell University. Her working experience had been in the public health and mental health areas.

In 1953, Miss Anderson became Director of Nursing at Good Samaritan. She says she first rejected the post of dean of the new college on the grounds that she lacked a Ph.D. degree. Doctor Arnold Tilden told her he could hire Ph.D.'s; what he wanted was "her experience and understanding in the field of nursing."

The committee selected to write the curriculum for the generic four-year program at Tempe was composed of Mrs. Josephine Steiner Barger, the former Director of Nursing at Good Samaritan Hospital; Dr. George M. Bateman, Professor of Chemistry at ASC; Mrs. Vurlyne Boan, Assistant Director of Nursing Education, Good Samaritan Hospital; Miss Margaret Elsik, Assistant Director of Nursing, Good Samaritan Hospital; Miss Rosamond Gabrielson, Assistant Director of Nursing, Good Samaritan Hospital; Mrs. Mary Pittman, Director of Nursing, Arizona State Hospital; Dr. Jesse Rannells, Professor of Home Economics at ASC; and the new director, later to become dean, Loretta Anderson. The new School of Nursing was organized within the ASC (ASU) College of Liberal Arts and later (1964) became a separate college.

By the mid–1960s the Good Samaritan School of Nursing and the training of interns at the hospital was costing the sponsors between $250,000 and $300,000 a year. The trustees, realizing it was only a matter of time until all nurses would be required to have a bachelor of science degree, ordered the school closed, and the last class was graduated in 1973. But this was not the end of Good Samaritan Hospital's contribution to education.

In 1980 Samaritan Health Service, in cooperation with Grand Canyon College, established the Samaritan College of Nursing with a four-year baccalaureate course. The students receive their academic instruction on the college campus and their clinical courses are coordinated with selected hospitals in the Phoenix area.

An in-house education center sponsored by Samaritan Health Service was established under the direction of Grace Middlebrook, R.N., Ed.D. The center offers courses of instruction in a variety of fields for employees of SHS anxious to upgrade their knowledge and advance in their profession. The philosophy of this new department is succinctly expressed in a foreword to the catalogue:

"We believe people are our greatest resource. We believe that every Samaritan Health Service employee should have a personal commitment to career-related educational development. We further believe that each individual has learning and growth potential which, when developed, offers the corporation increased productivity and the employee a greater sense of dignity. Evaluation of individual and organizational needs provides the criteria for educational program training."

The center helps to orient new employees, provides skill training, leadership and management development, and continuing education in a variety of areas, including critical care nursing, the problems of geriatrics, medical terminology, operating room nursing, motivational dynamics, public speaking, and perhaps a dozen more subjects.

The center sponsors seminars, brings in nationally recognized authorities, as well as utilizing in-house personnel, to present educational programs. Samaritan employees and others seeking to improve their skills and learning pay modest fees for the instruction and the workshops are self-supporting.

Stephen M. Morris, chief executive officer of the Samaritan system, is very pleased with the results obtained, and director Grace Middlebrook points out that such a service is made possible by the Samaritan system of hospitals.

"No single hospital could afford it—they wouldn't have enough clients—but the seven thousand employees of SHS keep us busy, and we have the satisfaction of knowing we are increasing the skills of our present employees and providing an opportunity for them to advance within the system."

CHAPTER 7

The Early Doctors

The quality and quantity of health care available to the people of the United States is vastly superior to that enjoyed by any other population in the world. Since 1920 rapid improvement in the art of the practice of medicine has dramatically increased life expectancy and almost totally banished the killers and cripplers which have plagued mankind throughout history. Diphtheria, smallpox, tuberculosis, poliomyelitis, typhoid fever are no longer high mortality threats.

New diagnostic techniques, improved laboratory work, antibiotics, advanced surgical skills, and a variety of improved anesthetics contribute to this change. Credit must be given to better medical education, research scientists laboring in teaching hospitals, the pharmaceutical industry, better communications, and the gradual appearance of medical specialists. It was not always so.

For at least the first three decades of the 20th Century, doctors had to be generalists. They were expected to deliver babies, mend broken bones, repair gunshot wounds, take out tonsils, and treat every type of infection or disease. There were doctors who never practiced medicine but, nevertheless, made a substantial contribution to the settlement and growth of Arizona. John T. Alsap, one of the original incorporators of the City of Phoenix, and James C. Douglas, who built the copper empire now known as Phelps Dodge, were both licensed in medicine. Pioneer Win Wylie was both a licensed doctor and a licensed lawyer, but he never practiced law. Dr. William M. Rudd, the grandfather of Congressman

Eldon Rudd, came to Springerville in 1876, practiced for ten years, studied law, left medicine, and became the first county judge in Apache County. For the most part, these early-day doctors were responsible for the organization of hospitals.

Dr. John B. Dennett, a graduate in medicine from Harvard University who came to Arizona in 1896, served on the original finance committee of the Deaconess Hospital and on the board of directors until 1923.

Dr. Ralph Fleetwood Palmer, with a medical degree from the University of Michigan, came to Arizona in 1901. He practiced in Prescott, moved to Camp Verde, and then to Roosevelt, where he was local surgeon for the Reclamation Service during the construction of the dam. Palmer and Joseph Madison Greer opened the first hospital in Mesa in 1913.

Dr. Prince Albert Melick, a graduate of Beaumont Medical College, came to Arizona in 1895 and built the Williams Hospital in 1897.

Dr. Meade Clyne, a graduate of Northwestern University, Chicago, came to Arizona in 1910 and three years later commenced operating the Arizona Hospital in Tucson.

Dr. Logan D. Dameron, a graduate of the Hospital College School of Medicine, Louisville, Kentucky, came to Arizona in 1892, helped organize the Maricopa County Medical Society and, as a Methodist layman, signed the deed conveying the land on East McDowell to the Deaconess Hospital. Dr. Dameron was Maricopa County Physician in the early 1920s and one of his duties was to personally quarantine those who suffered with contagious diseases.

Dr. E. Payne Palmer was graduated from Washington University in St. Louis and came to Phoenix in 1900. He made his first house calls on a bicycle.

Dr. Alexander M. Tuthill came to Arizona in 1901, was a member of the Constitutional Convention of 1910, and later served as Adjutant General of the Arizona National Guard.

Dr. William Clyde Ellis was graduated from the Medical School of Ohio at Cincinnati and commenced practicing his profession in Sardenia in 1899. In 1905 he left Ohio and travelled to Oklahoma, seeking a more benign climate for his wife. He entered farming and did very well raising broom corn, a crop new to that part of the country. But the effects of the change of climate were disappointing. In 1907 he came to Phoenix and reentered the practice of medicine. His daughter, Helen, remembers that for a time they lived almost in the open air, in two small canvas and wooden buildings located on Central Avenue just north of Indian School Road.

Dr. Ellis was a talented and compassionate physician and his practice grew rapidly. Despite Arizona's curative climate and the best of care, Mrs. Ellis died in 1915. A year or so later Dr. Ellis married the former Reba Blount, whose father, Frank J., was an early pioneer resident of Phoenix. The Blounts lived at 1302 North Central, and Dr. Ellis built a substantial brick three-story house at 1242 North Central. This residence is now occupied by the Arizona Historical Society.

When the new Deaconess Hospital was opened on McDowell Road on June 23, 1923, Janet Burns was general superintendent and J. A. Bowman was business manager. At the old building on North Third Avenue the organization of the medical staff had been quite casual. Now, as the trustees were told by Dr. Davis, "the hospital must be opened to all licensed physicians practicing in Maricopa County." Davis said a chief of staff must be named, a secretary, and committees formed to established guidelines and set standards for various hospital functions.

The trustees named Dr. W. C. Ellis chief of staff and Dr. Harry L. Goss secretary. Ellis formed a medical council, a surgical committee, a medical committee, a diagnostic committee, a records committee, and an obstetrics and nursing committee. To serve on the medical council with him, he named Dr. George P. Goodrich, a graduate of Rush Medical School who commenced his Arizona practice in Clifton and Morenci, then moved to Phoenix. Dr. E. Payne Palmer, Dr. Harry L. Goss and Dr. Stillman D. Little completed the medical council.

Dr. Charles Benjamin Palmer (who earned his medical degree at Johns Hopkins and commenced his Arizona practice in Naco in 1912), Dr. James R. Shupe, Dr. Willard Smith, Dr. Ancil Martin (who commenced practice in Phoenix in 1892 after graduating from Rush Medical College), and Dr. Goodrich made up the surgical committee. Doctors Frederick T. Fahlen, Harry B. Gudgel, Orville Harry Brown, Fred G. Holmes and Stillman D. Little were on the medical committee.

Pathologist Dr. Harlan P. Mills headed the diagnostic committee and named to serve with him were Doctors Ernest L. Hicks, Harry Goss, Alexander M. Tuthill and Charles S. Vivian.

The records committee was chaired by pathologist W. Warner Watkins and with him, Doctors Henry A. Hughes (who came to Phoenix in 1886 and was a charter member of the Arizona Medical Association), Henry T. Bailey, Thomas E. McCall and Harry J. Felch.

Doctors Mills and Watkins were tubercular patients at St. Luke's when they first came to Arizona. Later they formed an association with two other St. Luke's patients, Dr. Boynton and Dr. Horspool, and organized the city's first pathological laboratory.

Dr. Logan Dameron was on the obstetrics and nursing committee, with Doctors J. Wix Thomas, Arthur J. MacIntyre, Lewis Dysart and Lawrence H. Thayer.

The performance of hospital committees is vital to the quality of the health care provided. Dr. Ellis and the trustees had selected a good mix: older men with long established reputations, as well as some of the newer doctors who could be expected to contribute the latest in medical understanding. Fourteen of the 29 hospital committee members had practiced before statehood. Dr. J. Wix Thomas, who was then 66, was the oldest. Most of the men were in their middle 40's to early 50's. Goodrich was only 33.

Werter D. Shackelford, a doctor of dental surgery and a graduate of the Kansas Dental College, practiced his profession in Beloit from 1898 to 1910. His son, James Gordon, had frequent bouts with pneumonia and the family doctor recommended that Dr. Shackelford take his ailing son to a better climate. Planning to go to San Diego, Dr. Shackelford stopped in Phoenix to see pioneer dentist Dr. John Lentz, whom he had met at a dental convention in Denver. He was persuaded to take the dental boards and reestablished his practice in Phoenix. The Shackelfords lived just around the corner from the Ellises at 74 West Portland.

The Shackelford boy and the Ellis girl were childhood sweethearts. Gordon graduated from the School of Dentistry at Northwestern University in Chicago in June of 1923. He and Helen Ellis were married in September. Helen's father was chief of staff at the Good Samaritan Hospital and he immediately invited his new son-in-law to join that staff as an oral surgeon. Dr. J. Gordon Shackelford, the only surviving member of that original Good Samaritan Hospital staff, has some fond memories of those early days.

"About a week after Dr. Ellis appointed me, he came over and asked me to take care of a woman who was hospitalized with a fractured jaw. I protested that I had not done any fractures in practice. All I knew about it was what I had been taught in school and in the laboratories.

"I remember his saying, 'Son, I don't know anyone in this town who has had any experience reducing fractured jaws.'

"I went over to the hospital and saw the lady. She was from some place in Oregon and her jaw had been broken for about a month. I don't know how she stood the pain. We took her up to surgery, and just as I started, five or six staff doctors came in and asked if they could observe. I remember now it made me a little nervous, but I was afraid to say no.

"I started the procedure the way I had been taught, and God must have had me by the hand. Everything went smooth as silk. The lady did not have any swelling or soreness. She just got well. That got me started in the fractured jaw repair business and I did a lot of them, at both Good Sam and St. Joe's."

Dr. Shackelford, a very early aviation enthusiast and one of the first local pilots, suspended his dental practice in 1940 to become a civilian flight instructor at Thunderbird Field Number 1. The superiority of American pilots and American planes won World War II in Europe, and Dr. Shackelford helped train hundreds of those superior pilots. After the war he resumed the practice of dentistry but did not ask to go back on the staff of Good Samaritan.

He says, "We had some well trained, well qualified oral surgeons by this time."

Helen Shackelford remembers having her appendix removed in the old Angeny Building on North Third Avenue, after it had been taken over by the deaconesses.

"The operating room was on the first floor, as I remember it. There was no elevator and they had to carry me upstairs to my room on a stretcher. But the nurses made me comfortable, my father was there, and it is not an unpleasant memory."

Dr. Shackelford says that when he went on the staff at Good Samaritan, in the new building on McDowell Road, the facilities and the quality of care offered compared very favorably with that available in the big hospitals in Chicago where he had taken part of his training.

"Mrs. Sexson was in charge of the nursing. She was a martinet, but the care they provided was excellent. The hospital was always in financial difficulty but, as I remember, we kind of expected it to be that way. Many of the patients could not pay but, at Good Sam and at St. Joe's, we took care of them anyway."

Phoenix was still a very small town, but it was growing. In 1923 the population was just over 31,000. Ten years later it was 48,118. By 1928 the need for additional hospital space could no longer be ignored, so the trustees went again to the community asking for financial help. A total of $120,000 was raised. The Phoenix Title and Trust Company subscribed to $125,000 in bonds secured by a first mortgage, and in 1930 ground was broken for a new wing.

The new wing, east of the central reception and administrative area, conformed in appearance to the original West Wing and increased the hospital capacity to 200 beds. It was opened January 25, 1931. That year the hospital served 3,439 patients.

Towards the end of that third decade of the 20th Century there had been some remarkable changes in the downtown area, with the construction of the 12-story Professional Building and the completion of the Westward Ho Hotel three blocks to the north. But when the full force of the Depression struck Arizona, there was no new building and for a number of years the old Main Post Office at Central and Fillmore was a boarded up hole in the ground.

In 1932 the voters of Arizona favored Franklin Delano Roosevelt for President over Herbert Hoover and elected B. B. Moeur, a medical doctor from Tempe, governor. There were 152,393 registered voters, but only 119,124 bothered to go to the polls.

In 1933, Walter H. Bimson, an officer with the Harris Trust Company in Chicago, moved to Phoenix to become the new chief executive officer of the Valley Bank. More than any other single individual, Walter Bimson helped Arizona climb out of the Great Depression. It was said that before Bimson came the bankers only wanted to loan money to people who did not need it. The new policies of loaning money to credit-worthy individuals to build homes, buy automobiles and make household purchases had a profound effect on the struggling little farming community. In 1933, the three "Cs"—cotton, cattle and copper—were the mainstays of the state's economy. Walter Bimson's son, Earl, was named to the board of trustees of Good Samaritan in 1969, became chairman of the board in 1976, and still serves on the board of directors of Samaritan Medical Foundation.

In 1932 admissions at Good Samaritan Hospital dropped by more than 11 percent and, with the burden of the debt for the new wing, the trustees were constantly scrambling for funds. But somehow, frequently with the help of loans from the Valley Bank, the doors remained open, and in 1936 operating income exceeded expenses for the first time in more than six years.

The new members who came on the hospital's board of directors were chosen for their influence in the community and their concern for the future of Phoenix. Isaac Diamond resigned and his nephew Harold took his place. E. W. Montgomery, superintendent of the Phoenix Union High School and Junior College and a prominent Methodist, was named to the board in 1929. Active Southern Methodist layman B. F. McGough, whose Miller's Cafeteria on Adams was a very popular eating place, joined the board in 1931. Governor John Phillips came back on the board after his term as the State's chief executive, and lawyer John Gust was named to fill the vacancy caused by the death of his partner, Judge Frank O. Smith. The business community was better represented by J. C. Elms, C. C. Jenkins, and B. F. Carter of Vinson Carter Electric. Lorel Stapley, of the prominent Mesa family, represented the Mormon community. And Cleveland industrialist John C. Lincoln, who had established a home in Paradise Valley and was later to become the great benefactor of the John C. Lincoln Hospital in north Phoenix, joined the Good Samaritan board of trustees.

St. Joseph's in Phoenix and Southside in Mesa had their own problems, and many of the practicing physicians and surgeons made substantial anonymous contributions on a regular basis to keep the hospitals open.

With the facilities then available to them, these early doctors truly performed miracles. They packed the surgical wounds to stop bleeding, inserted drains, and were personally involved with the outcome.

Dr. L. D. Beck, who commenced practice in Phoenix in the mid-30s, recalls a case of a man who was brought to the Emergency Room suffering from a gunshot wound at the hands of a local deputy sheriff. L. D. says, "The bullet went right through the man's liver. We transfused him, removed the blood from the abdominal cavity, and I packed the wound with what we used to call a lap pad. It was about four or five inches wide, 20 or 30 inches long, and had a ring on each end so that if you left one inside the X-ray could locate it.

"I cut off one of the rings and packed almost all of that material into the wound until the bleeding finally stopped. We tied up what vessels we could, partially sewed up the wound, and left the packing in. I slept at the hospital that night. Every hour or so I would check on him. The next morning when he was awake he said, 'Doc, when can I get out?' He was feeling pretty good because we had continued the transfusions all night. I told him he couldn't go until I had the packing out and his wound was healed. I removed it about two inches at a time every day. He was out of the hospital and gone in two weeks. And whatever trouble he was in with the law, they forgot about it."

It was in the '30s that the age of specialization was born. Dr. Joseph Madison Greer went east to learn more about orthopedic surgery. When he returned he was one of the best qualified for that specialty in the state, but it was still necessary for him to take care of patients with other problems.

Dr. William Oscar Sweek, a gruff, good-hearted tyrant who had been selected by the Grunow family to head and operate the clinic of that name, came into the hospital one morning after Greer had done some orthopedic surgery and noted the doctor was scheduled for some tonsillectomies in the afternoon. Sweek waited until Greer was within earshot and then observed in a loud tone of voice, "What the hell's going on here—an orthopedic surgeon taking out tonsils?"

"We didn't have many of the things then we have now," Beck says, "and I think that made us try a little harder. There weren't many doctors. We were all good friends and the practice had its lighter moments."

Beck recalls that Coit I. Hughes, son of Henry Hughes and one of the first native-born Arizona doctors, delivered a baby one night for a black family he had known for many years. The delivery was at home. The mother was doing very well but Hughes was worried about the baby, so he brought the infant into the emergency room. It was late at night and there was only one hospital attendant on duty—a lady who had to answer the telephone, admit patients, and call doctors as they were needed. "I was in the room when Coit came in with this black child in his arms and said he wanted the baby admitted. The attendant began asking questions and filling out the forms and after a few minutes of this, without looking up, she said, 'Are you the father?' "

Dr. Paul Jarrett, who was born on West Monroe and went to the Methodist Sunday School where Lulu Clifton was his teacher, remembers Coit Hughes as a kindly, competent physician, totally devoted to his patients.

"When I was a medical student," Jarrett says, "Coit Hughes would sometimes let me accompany him on his house calls. He would always explain to the patients that I was a student who needed to learn and ask their permission for me to be there. One night we went together to deliver a baby. Home deliveries were commonplace. When we finished, the father, who as I remember had a crippled leg, brought a ten dollar bill to Dr. Hughes and said, 'It's all we have. I want you to take it and, as soon as I can, I'll pay whatever the rest is I owe you'."

Jarrett says Dr. Hughes put his arm around the young man and said, "Son, you keep this ten dollar bill and buy that new mother there a present."

Dr. Jarrett served as chief of staff of Good Samaritan Hospital in 1956 and 1957.

In those years, when Phoenix was a very small community, the doctors were very visible, dominant figures. There were two amusing stories circulated about Dr. Joseph Madison Greer. Greer was a very positive personality, a skilled physician and surgeon, and quite active in the community outside of his medical practice.

It is told that one of Dr. Greer's patients called him late at night. The lady said she had been reading in bed and she had dislocated her jaw. When Dr. Greer arrived, the lady was sitting in bed and her reading material had fallen to the floor. The doctor picked it up. The patient had been reading Mary Baker Eddy's book on Christian Science. Greer opened the pages and began reading aloud, not looking at the suffering patient. After a minute or two he put down the book, looked at her, and said, "Hasn't that jaw gone back in place yet?" The patient did not think it was very humorous! Greer wrapped his thumbs with gauze and reduced her dislocation.

Greer, the first orthopedic surgeon, was called on to work in outlying hospitals, and once a week he would ride the train to Wickenburg to take care of patients in that area. He told this story on himself.

"I was driving down Central, in a hurry to get to the station to catch the train to Wickenburg, when I hit another car. I did not have time to stop and explain, so I ran around to the other driver, handed him my card, and said, 'I'm Dr. Greer. Call me at my office.' " The driver of the car looked at the card and then at me. He said, "Doctor? Doctor? I don't need a doctor. Where's the man that hit me?" In telling of the incident, Dr. Greer said, "That was the fastest bit of ambulance chasing I ever did."

Dr. E. Henry (Hank) Running, an early-day pediatrician who commenced his practice in Phoenix in 1936, remembers J. O. Sexson more as a businessman than an administrator. "Mrs. Sexson, who was with the School of Nursing when I came, was a very beautiful, charming lady and she knew a lot about hospitals and nursing. J. O. was a very persuasive talker, and since most of the men on the board of trustees knew very little about hospital problems, they relied on J. O. In the fall of 1943, the medical staff had a number of grievances with the administration. They named Louis Baldwin, a very competent internist; James Lytton-Smith, and me to carry the complaints to the administrator and the trustees.

"We had an appointment to meet with E. W. Montgomery, John Gust, and Sexson. When I arrived at the hospital I was told to go upstairs to the nursery to care for a newborn. I found the baby normal and healthy cradled in an orange crate because all of the bassinets in the nursery were full.

"When I got back downstairs the meeting was in progress, and J. O. had just about persuaded Lytton-Smith and Baldwin that our complaints were unfounded and everything in the hospital was in good order. Of course, Montgomery and Gust were agreeing with Sexson.

"I said, 'Well, if everything is fine in the hospital and we don't need any improvements or any more room, please tell me why it is that the first grandchild of these two gentlemen, Mr. Gust and Mr. Montgomery, is lying in an orange crate on the floor in the nursery?'

"J. O. bristled and said, 'That can't be so! It's not so! It couldn't be so!'

"I said, 'Well, J. O., there's an easy way to settle this. Come with me, gentlemen.' I led them back upstairs and there was the Gust baby in an orange crate on the floor of the nursery.

"I have always cherished the notion that this was a turning point at Good Samaritan. I think from that time until they built their new building, there was always a jackhammer going, or a carpenter working, or a painter on the premises whenever I went to the hospital."

Running, who finished his final semester of undergraduate studies at the University of Arizona in 1930, says, "I had tuberculosis of the glands in my neck from drinking my grandfather's beautiful raw milk in South Dakota. I came out here, my neck stopped draining, my nose dried up, and it was a wonderful spring. I knew then, when I completed my medical education I was going to practice in Phoenix."

Running, who retired in 1983, has some pleasant memories of those early Depression years. "I was here more than a year before I could hire an office girl and when I did I could only pay her $12.00 a week.

"I told my mother I had to get a faster car, because back then when a child was sick, the parents would call two or three doctors and the first one who reached the house was the one who got paid.

"The advances in the art of healing during my practice are almost incomprehensible," Running says, "and perhaps the one which has gone almost unnoticed is the eradication of contagious diseases.

"When I came here there was one small contagious ward out behind St. Joseph's Hospital. There was no other place to send the diphtherians, the scarlet fevers, or the patients with polio and smallpox. Now they are all gone. The contagious hospitals where I trained have been closed for years."

Running, who helped establish the first crippled children's home in Arizona, believes the new techniques sometimes overwhelm common sense. "Nobody puts a sick kid to bed anymore. We give them an antibiotic and some aspirin and send them off to school. We are all too eager to reduce the fever. Fever is nature's way of fighting infection. Nobody uses posture drainage anymore, or saline solution irrigation."

Running says he quit making house calls when he had to go to the playground and pull the kid off the swing, but he concedes the doctors have much more to work with than when he commenced practice.

"We do many of the same things now we did then, but we do them better. We have better techniques and tools. It got to the point where I said I didn't mind making a house call if the kid wasn't really sick. If the problem was serious, I wanted him in my office where I had all the armamentaria of my practice."

Running says the doctors of today are unquestionably better trained, "but we had good men then. Hillary Ketcherside, whose father and grandfather were doctors in Yuma in the very early days; Jess Hamer, who was a leader in the AMA; Charlie Palmer and Bill Sweek were good surgeons. This was before we had any refrigeration in the surgeries and Bill Sweek wore two pair of boots when he operated. One pair, the right size and a pair of rubber boots considerably oversized. He packed the space between with crushed ice. He said it kept him from perspiring and possibly contaminating an open wound."

Running thinks the new techniques, new drugs, and new apparatus are largely responsible for the increased cost of health care. "We've got ways of keeping almost anyone alive. Our immunizations and our health programs have gotten us out of the routine contagious type of diseases. We are now in the very advanced surgical repair business, with transplants, neonatology, cardiology. We have lengthened the life span and this older population is particularly susceptible to those problems which demand the most expensive form of treatment. But as long as there is any humanity involved, we are not going to be like the eskimos and put them on the ice floe and let them float away, or have dying houses like the Chinese. We are going to treat them, and it is not all bad. Today you can get a new hip for around $10,000. When I started practice, if you had a bad hip the doctors told you to buy a cane and take some pain killers. When the arteries feeding the heart became occluded, the patient died. Now we do a double or triple bypass and the patient lives."

Another development which has impacted severely on the practice of medicine is the growth and the number of malpractice suits. Running says, "There probably isn't a research center that doesn't have something good going for it in the developmental stage right now. In a few years from now, if that isn't included in your armamentaria and you haven't done this test or don't have the machine to run it, and you run into a little trouble, some smart lawyer is going to say, 'How come you didn't do the bedpan raising time on this thing?' "

Dr. Paul Jarrett remembers that in those early days at Good Sam there was a general practitioner named Paul Armour. Whenever Armour was waiting for a patient in labor, he would occupy his time playing the hospital organ. Dr. Grace Middlebrook remembers the organ music was carried on speakers at a number of the nurses' stations. "We always knew when Armour had a bird on the nest," she says.

Armour discontinued this practice because one of the nurses fancied herself as a whistler, and when he played she always came down to join him. He did not think much of her whistling. He bought an organ, gave it to St. Luke's hospital and did most of his playing there.

The list of early-day physicians could go on and on: Tommy Woodman, an exceptionally talented surgeon; Charlie Borah, the Olympic gold medal winner who practiced oral surgery at Good Samaritan and was both a qualified dentist and qualified physician; Carlos C. Craig, who is still in active practice; Ben Pat Frissell, who practiced internal medicine with Louis Baldwin; surgeon Tom Bate, whose father and uncle were pioneer photographers in Phoenix and Prescott; Floyd Sharp, one of the first specialists in obstetrics and gynecology; Kim Bannister, who was a great amateur golfer and a good doctor; Charles Vivian; Sy Bloomhardt, who was almost as good a polo player as he was a physician; and Eugene Gatterdam, who came to Prescott to care for the veterans of World War I and earned a considerable reputation as one of the first allergists in the Southwest.

CHAPTER 8

War and Growth

When Hitler's panzer divisions rolled into Poland in September, 1939, Arizona had almost recovered from the effects of the Great Depression. Phoenix was still a parochial little city, farming was the economic base, there were fewer than 60,000 residents. The city limits were Thomas Road on the north, 19th Avenue on the west, 16th Street on the east, and Harrison Street on the south, with the exception of the area between Seventh Avenue and Seventh Street, where the southern limits had been extended to Buckeye Road.

The Phoenix Country Club at Seventh Street and Thomas, outside the city limits, was the center of social activity. Good Samaritan Hospital, with its new East Wing, was the largest in the Valley.

All commercial activity was centered in the downtown area between Third Street and Third Avenue, Jefferson and Van Buren. Diamond's (The Boston Store) was at the corner of Second Street and Washington, Korrick's (The New York Store) at First Street and Washington next to Goldwater's — where Barry and Bob were carrying on the family tradition of "The Best Always." The leading furniture stores were Dorris-Heyman's at the corner of First Street and Adams, and Barrow's at the corner of First Street and Jefferson. On Central, McDougall and Cassou, Vic Hanny's and Goldberg's catered to the fashion needs of men.

The restaurants were the Grand Cafe on Adams between Central and First Avenue, the American Kitchen just south of Adams on Central, Miller's Cafeteria on West Adams, Donofrio's on the ground floor of the Security Building, and the Green Gables. Bob Gosnell, whose family had a small women's ready-to-wear shop in the downtown area, originally opened the Green Gables in a tiny all wooden building way out in the country at Thomas and 24th Street. After the war they replaced the original building with a handsome stone structure resembling an old English castle.

Riverside Park, just north of the Salt River on Central Avenue, with its ballroom and swimming pool, was the favorite recreation spot. Three miles east on Thomas Road, The Beach, a swimming pool fed constantly with fresh water from a Salt River Valley Water Users' pump, was the preferred swimming hole. The San Carlos at Central and Monroe, the old Adams at Central and Adams, the Westward Ho at Fillmore and Central, the Luhrs at Central and Jefferson, and the Jefferson across the street (owned by Salim Ackel) were the hotels.

On the south side of East Jefferson and on East Madison Street between Fourth Street and Central, there were a dozen or so establishments calling themselves hotels or rooming houses, but they catered exclusively to male clients.

City government was run by five commissioners who elected their own mayor. There was a city manager, but he had to be a resident of Phoenix when he was hired, and any three commissioners could control city politics. City managers and chiefs of police were hired and fired with great regularity.

Most of the downtown buildings had refrigerated air conditioning. Others had the earlier evaporative coolers. But only a few homes out of every hundred had any sort of air cooling. When school closed in May or June, the families left for the mountains or the seashore, and business activity went into hibernation for three months. As one old-timer put it, "There was no push to get it done today because you could always do it tomorrow or next week and no one else was going to try to get ahead of you."

The battle fronts were more than 7,000 miles away but the war had a profound effect on the little desert city in Central Arizona. President Franklin Delano Roosevelt talked peace but began his preparations for war. In 1940, the federal government announced plans to develop new air bases to train Allied pilots and to expand our own air forces. Locations in Texas, California and Arizona were favored because of prevailing clear weather. Much of the year the air over Arizona is as bumpy as a corduroy road, but the almost year-round good visibility and the influence of

FORT MCDOWELL
On the Verde River. It was while he was hauling hay for the cavalry horses at this military outpost that Jack Swilling conceived his plan for irrigated agriculture in the Salt River Valley.
—Photograph from the Historical Collection
of Herb and Dorothy McLaughlin

HOLSUM BAKERY
West Washington Street, Ed Eisele and Alfred Becker.
—Photograph from the Historical Collection
of Herb and Dorothy McLaughlin

STATE CAPITOL
About 1901
        —Photograph from the Historical Collection
          of Herb and Dorothy McLaughlin

OSTRICHES
When ostrich plumes were fashionable, the production of these adornments was an important part of the Valley's economy.
        —Photograph from the Historical Collection
          of Herb and Dorothy McLaughlin

FIRST METHODIST CHURCH
Corner of Second Avenue and Monroe.

FORD HOTEL
In the foreground. The spire of the Methodist Church can be seen in the background.
—Photograph from the Historical Collection
of Herb and Dorothy McLaughlin

COL JAMES H. MCCLINTOCK
Publisher, historian and Valley leader.
—Stephen Shadegg

JUDGE JOSEPH H. KIBBEY
Judge of the Territorial Supreme Court, Territorial Governor, he wrote the articles of incorporation for the Salt River Valley Water Users, the nation's first federal reclamation project.

JOHN Y. T. SMITH
Who hired Jack Swilling to deliver hay harvested in the Salt River bottom lands to Fort McDowell.
—Stephen Shadegg

JOHN R. NORTON
Superintendent of the Arizona Canal who, with Breakenridge and McClintock, surveyed the original Roosevelt Dam site.
—Stephen Shadegg

DORRIS OPERA HOUSE
The plans to build a storage reservoir at the Roosevelt site were developed at town meetings held here.
—Stephen Shadegg

ELECTRIC STREET CAR
Moses Hazeltine Sherman developed the street railway system in Phoenix, horse-drawn cars first and then they were electrified.
—Photograph from the Historical Collection
of Herb and Dorothy McLaughlin.

YMCA
On West Monroe. The center of activity.
—Photograph from the Historical Collection
of Herb and Dorothy McLaughlin

PHOENIX CITY HALL
On the square between First and Second Streets, Washington and Jefferson.
—Photograph from the Historical Collection
of Herb and Dorothy McLaughlin

VALLEY BANK OF PHOENIX
Started by Colonel William Christy, Moses
Hazeltine Sherman and their associates.
—Photograph from the Historical Collection
of Herb and Dorothy McLaughlin

HEARD BUILDING
—Photograph from the Historical Collection
of Herb and Dorothy McLaughlin

CHARLES STAUFFER
Who, with Wesley W. Knorpp, owned and
published *The Arizona Republic* and *The Phoenix Gazette*.

WESLEY WILLIAM KNORPP
Publisher and co-owner of *The Arizona Repub-
lic/The Phoenix Gazette;* member of the board
of trustees, Good Samaritan Hospital for 45
years.

ORIGINAL TUBERCULAR COTTAGE AT ST. LUKE'S HOME

RIGHT REVEREND J. W. ATWOOD
First Bishop of the Missionary District of Arizona Protestant Episcopal Church who as a vicar at Trinity Cathedral Church raised the funds and established St. Luke's Home for tuberculars.

REVEREND BERTRAND COCKS
Served as administrator of St. Luke's Home for more than 30 years.

U. S. Senator Carl Hayden resulted in the establishing of Luke Field near Litchfield Park, west of Phoenix, Williams Field near Chandler, and Davis-Monthan Field at Tucson.

These advanced flying schools were operated by the Army Air Forces and trained combat pilots. Primary and secondary training was contracted out to civilian schools. Thunderbird Field was established north of Glendale, Falcon Field near Mesa, and there was a base at Marana, midway between Phoenix and Tucson. Thousands of young men from colder eastern climates came to Arizona to learn to fly, and were made welcome by the people of Phoenix.

Miss Luella Archer, who had a mansion at the corner of Thomas Road and Central Avenue, sponsored dances and parties and invited the young ladies of Phoenix to come and entertain the soldiers. After Pearl Harbor, training was intensified. The Cadet Nurses Program at Good Samaritan Hospital brought more than 50 students from other states.

Recognizing the vulnerability of the Pacific Coast, manufacturers were encouraged to move inland, and AiResearch established a plant adjacent to Sky Harbor Airport. Alcoa built a plant to manufacture aluminum on West Van Buren.

There was a national speed limit of 35 miles an hour. Almost all commercial and residential construction was prohibited. Good Samaritan Hospital was denied permission to purchase a new X-ray machine. Tires and gasoline were rationed. Only a relatively few automobiles were built, as Detroit turned its energies to supporting the war effort. It was a time of tragedy and triumph.

The battleship U.S.S. Arizona had been a victim of the Japanese attack on Pearl Harbor. A number of those who died were from Arizona. Married women, who had never before worked outside the home, entered the factories to become welders, and "Rosie the Riveter" was a national hero. The people of the United States were drawn together. Executives contributed their skills to the war effort and proudly accepted a dollar a year as their pay. Doctors, dentists and nurses were called into service. The Professional Building lost more than half of its tenants. And because the medical community of Phoenix was so small in 1940, those who were unable to serve did double duty here at home.

General George C. Patton trained his desert troops between Hyder, Arizona and Indio, California. At Fort Huachuca, that old

Indian war cavalry post in southern Arizona, 50,000 troops were trained for combat.

Beef was rationed and Arizona ranchers had cattle to sell at good prices. Cotton was in great demand and the acreage was increased each year from 1941 to 1945. In time of war copper is a strategic metal so the mines throughout the state were working double shifts.

Phoenix and all of Maricopa County struggled to provide housing and other services for the new population. Hundreds of civilian flight instructors came here from all over the nation to teach in the primary and secondary schools. They brought their wives and families with them and accepted whatever housing was available. Many of the student pilots at Luke and Williams were married and had families. Because of wartime restrictions, no new houses or apartments could be built. Restaurants could not expand. The downtown movie theatres, Mrs. Archer Linde's concert series, and the Phoenix Little Theatre operating in an old stable on the Heard property at Central and McDowell, all enjoyed overflow audiences.

The red light district in the old tenderloin area called the "Deuce" expanded to satisfy the soldiers and, at one point, the commandants of Luke and Williams declared the city off limits because of the high rate of venereal infection.

This brought an immediate reaction from the city's businessmen to put pressure on the mayor and the police and, for a time, vice was rigidly controlled.

This new population increased the patient load at Good Samaritan and between January 1, 1937 and April 1, 1942, the hospital trustees were able to pay off $172,000 of bonds which had been issued to build the new East Wing. The government contributed more than $50,000 for the training of cadet nurses. In 1943, J. O. Sexson and the trustees proposed building a new dormitory residence for the girls in nurses' training. The federal government agreed to put up $150,000 of the estimated $300,000 cost and an architect was engaged to prepare the plans.

In November of 1944 the trustees were confronted with a major crisis. Nine highly respected doctors on the medical staff made a formal complaint about the inadequacy of the hospital's services. The committee which brought the matter before the board was composed of Doctors Louis B. Baldwin, Ben Pat Frissell, F. C. Jordan, Robert Stephens, Howell Randolph, W. H. Woern,

Henry Running, Warner W. Watkins and Fred Holmes. They did not fault J. O. Sexson or the hospital administration. The government's refusal to permit them to buy needed X-ray equipment and make improvements in pathological facilities could no longer be accommodated.

When the war finally ended and the nation began to return to a civilian economy, the pent-up demand for consumer goods supported expansion and full employment in Arizona — particularly in Phoenix and Tucson. Many of those transients who had come to serve in the armed forces or work in the wartime industries decided they liked the casual lifestyle and the wonderful climate of the West. Hundreds of pilots who trained at Luke and "Willie" went home just long enough to marry their childhood sweethearts and come back to Arizona.

In 1945, Eugene C. Pulliam came to Phoenix from Indianapolis and bought *The Arizona Republic* and *The Phoenix Gazette* from Charlie Stauffer and Wes Knorpp. These two — mild-mannered, gentle, compassionate Charlie Stauffer and hard working, hard driving, tenacious Wes Knorpp — had been like a good cop/bad cop pair; with Knorpp ramrodding most civic improvements, using the admitted power of the newspapers to get things done, and Stauffer, the conciliator, smoothing ruffled feathers, moderating much of the pain which accompanies growth. Their departure from the public scene was viewed with considerable apprehension by the local business community, which had learned to count on the active participation of the newspapers when something needed to be done.

Gene Pulliam brought something more than his money from Indianapolis. Like the new convert, he was more enthusiastic and steadfast in support of his adopted community than many of the old-timers. He brought a fresh perspective. He could see what needed to be done, and he was not inhibited by any memories of failed past attempts.

When Pulliam came, more than half the urban population lived outside the city limits, and that area constituted the largest unsewered city population in the United States. Pulliam put on the pressure to expand the city limits, to extend the sewers, to enlarge, improve and modernize the city water system, and to reform the city government. Gene Pulliam, sometimes irascible, often thought of as bullheaded, was a builder who put a mark of excellence on the Phoenix community which will never be erased.

Throughout these years of growth Good Samaritan Hospital had struggled to keep up with the new demands. Some of the old-timers on the board of trustees died and were replaced by others who had demonstrated the same strong sense of community responsibility which had distinguished the board from its inception.

In 1945 Sexson and Knorpp persuaded their fellow Kiwanian M. O. (Mac) Best to accept election to the board of trustees of the hospital.

Best had come to Phoenix in 1924 to work with Dean Stanley, one of the state's more successful produce growers. During the 20 intervening years he had become one of the real movers and shakers in the Phoenix community — the Southwest's largest produce grower and shipper, chairman of the board of Arizona Public Service Company, director of the Valley National Bank and Salt River Valley Water Users, and a member of the Arizona Board of State University Regents.

Mac Best was one of the leaders in the effort to bring supplemental water into Arizona, a strong supporter of what is now ASU, first president of the University Foundation, and an organizer of the Sun Angels. He brought energy, experience and commitment to the hospital board, and ultimately served as president of the Good Samaritan trustees.

In 1946 the new Nurses Home was completed by contractor P. W. Womack. The total price for the original structure was $224,933. That year the hospital had $50,000 over and above current needs. The trustees decided to open a savings account and put the money away until it could be spent for improvements in building and equipment. The Phoenix National Bank offered to pay the hospital one-half of one percent interest a year on the building fund. The trustees opted to buy government securities because they were paying seven-eighths of one percent per year. In 1947, the trustees raised J. O. Sexson's salary to $1,000 a month. After 24 years of service, his annual salary was $12,000.

One unintended consequence of the great world conflict was the rapid development of new techniques in medicine and surgery. A whole new family of drugs dramatically reduced the possibility of infection. Lifesaving surgical techniques developed on the battle front became routine procedures at home.

In World War II, Dr. Paul Singer was an assistant to the chief surgeon at a hospital in Ireland at the time of the Normandy invasion. He was assigned to one of the landing craft ferrying troops, tanks and ammunition. Singer says the vessels, after they were un-loaded, were converted to field hospitals with 300 beds. "We were set up for surgery and that is what I did. I made seven runs and, because we could treat and stabilize the wounded immediately, thousands of lives were saved." Dr. Singer subsequently became chief of staff at Good Samaritan Hospital, was elected to the State Senate from Maricopa County, and appointed to the Arizona Board of Regents.

That war which changed the history of the world had perhaps an even more profound effect upon Arizona's capital city. The military training camps, the war industries, brought in a new population, and the increasing availability of refrigerated air conditioning mitigated the tyranny of summertime heat.

After more than 20 years of constant financial struggle, members of the Good Samaritan Hospital board (many of whom had served in that position since the founding of the institution) could feel confident of the future. The hospital was a monument to J. O. Sexson's managerial talents. The board purchased an annuity to cover Sexson's retirement, which would pay him an income of $200 a month after his 70th birthday. It also authorized Sexson to find and hire an assistant administrator.

Guy M. Hanner was born in Sumner, Iowa. His father, a Methodist minister, sent Guy to Cornell College in Mount Vernon, Iowa and hoped he would devote his life to church work.

When he completed his education, Guy Hanner wanted to go to Brazil, where he believed there was great commercial opportunity. His father opposed the notion, and they reached a compromise. Guy would go to Oklahoma and work in his uncle's bank. He married the sister of one of the bank's board of directors. When his wife contracted tuberculosis, they moved to Colorado Springs, Colorado for her health. And the young man who preferred banking to preaching became, first, business manager, and then administrator of the Bethel Hospital.

In 1941 Hanner left Colorado Springs to become administrator of the Desert Sanitarium in Tucson. But he maintained a home in Colorado Springs and Mrs. Hanner divided her time between Colorado and Tucson. Her turberculosis was arrested but not cured. In June, 1943, he went to work for the U.S. Government on the War Relocation Authority and was involved in the administration of the internment camps where Pacific Coast Japanese were quartered. In February of 1944 Hanner went to Hilo, Hawaii to become administrator of the Memorial Hospital there.

In 1945 J. O. Sexson was 65 years old. His daughter Edith Sexson Brown, who later married F. A. Faville, had a responsible position with Central Arizona Light and Power (predecessor to APS). His son Paul, who was graduated with honors from Stanford University, married Barry Goldwater's sister Carolyn, and from 1933 to 1936 served as private secretary to former President Herbert Hoover, and was public relations manager for the Lockheed Aircraft Corporation in Burbank, California.

Sexson had been aware of Hanner's work as a hospital administrator in Colorado. They were both members of the American College of Hospital Administrators. Hanner had been president of the Colorado Hospital Association and the American Protestant Hospital Association. When Sexson offered him the job at Good Samaritan, at a salary of $6,000 per year, Hanner accepted. He came to work as an assistant administrator in 1945 and was promoted to administrator in 1948 when Sexson retired. For someone less competent, less dedicated to providing patients with the best possible health care, it might have been a very difficult situation because the hospital's board of directors made Sexson president of the board. And, while on paper Hanner had the complete responsibility for operating the hospital, his old boss was at the top of the ladder where he might have second-guessed every decision Hanner made. Actually, there were no conflicts. Hanner was only four years younger than Sexson, and both men were totally dedicated to making Good Samaritan a leader in the hospital field.

Hanner, like Sexson, was bent on enlarging the hospital's physical facilities and improving the medical service offered. He got along well with the board of trustees and the medical staff, and was just as careful with the hospital's dollars as Sexson had been. But he did make changes.

Between 1940 and 1950 the population of Phoenix almost doubled, moving from 65,414 to 106,818. The Charter Reform Movement started by Mayor Ray Busey and sponsored by, among others, Barry Goldwater, Nick Udall, Harry and Newt Rosenzweig, had replaced the old commission government, with the council and mayor making policy decisions and a professional city manager in charge of day-to-day operations. The Charter Government committee disbanded after each election and then re-formed in time for the next election. It drafted prominent men and women to serve on the City Council. There was an unwritten understanding that no one would be asked to serve more than two terms, four years. The Police Department became an exemplary law enforcement group. There was no graft, very little vice, taxes were kept low, Department of Water and Sewers was upgraded. Eastern manufacturers, looking for new locations, moved to Phoenix. Climate was a part of it. The lifestyle was attractive. But, most of all, these easterners were fed up with politics and graft.

Before General Electric decided to establish a plant in Phoenix, two corporate officers came out to evaluate the city. They were pleased with what they found: a relatively modest tax rate, adequate city services, and a healthy business climate. Just to make sure the city government was incorruptible, they rented a car, deliberately violated a traffic law, and were given a ticket. One of the executives went to the Mayor — at the time Jack Williams, who later was to become Governor of Arizona — and bitterly complained about his ticket. Here he was, he said, almost ready to decide to build a new plant in Phoenix and provide a thousand new jobs, and this overzealous traffic cop had given him a ticket for a minor infraction of the city code.

Mayor Williams expressed his hope that General Electric would come to Phoenix. He said, "I can't fix the ticket for you because we don't do that. I'll pay it for you, if that will make you any happier."

G.E. paid the ticket and moved to Phoenix.

Good Samaritan Hospital, under the administration of Guy Hanner, kept pace with the growth and expansion of the population. In 1952, the South Wing was expanded, the first and second floors of the hospital remodeled, and a new East Wing was started. Cost of construction was estimated to be $1,350,000. Of this amount, $494,500 in Hill-Burton funds was made available.

Trustee C. O. Vosburgh of Buckeye made a personal contribution of $45,000 to construct a small chapel in the new wing, and the Phoenix Title and Trust Company contributed stained glass windows which were the outstanding architectural feature of this small house of prayer and meditation.

The windows had originally been given to the First Methodist Church by Lloyd B. Christy, who was one of the original incorporators of the Deaconess Hospital and served as trustee and secretary from 1911 to 1944. During those 33 years he attended at least 450 meetings, and in the early days the minutes are in his handwriting. When the First Methodist Church was torn down, the Title and Trust Company acquired the windows, having this future use in mind. When the new wing was completed the hospital had 320 beds and 42 bassinets.

As was his predecessor, J. O. Sexson, Guy Hanner was a man of tremendous energy and had a clear vision of what Good Samaritan's goal of service should be. During the Sexson years the hospital was almost constantly in the red, but the economic growth of Phoenix had changed this, there were funds available to make improvements. Hanner instituted patient surveys to discover how the hospital could better serve this group of clients. The first improvement resulting from the survey was to establish the nurses' station in one of the rooms. They had been located in the hallways, where the patients complained of the constant noise.

In 1954, Good Samaritan established the first post-anesthesia, or recovery room, adjacent to the surgical unit to be installed in an Arizona hospital — a practice which is now standard in the industry. Hanner was a leader in the effort to establish a four-year baccalaureate program for nursing education at what is now ASU, and he urged his Director of Nursing, Loretta Anderson, to take the position of director at the new school when it was offered to her by Dr. Arnold Tilden.

Miss Anderson has some very vivid recollections of her conversation with the administrator which led to her acceptance of the new post. Loretta Anderson had come to Good Samaritan in 1953 to become Associate Director of Nursing under Josephine Steiner Barger, who was planning to leave the hospital within a year.

"Guy called me into his office one morning in 1957. He knew that Dr. Tilden had offered me the post of dean in the soon to be established school at Tempe. I had said I wasn't interested. I didn't think it would be fair to leave Good Samaritan without giving at least a year's notice. So Guy asked me what my career goals were. I told him I always liked to work with students. He then asked me if the Director of Nursing job at the hospital was something I would like to stay with. I said no. I felt I was more of a community person than a hospital person. He said, 'Then I would advise you to go over there and talk to them and take the job. But, wait a minute. When you go, there are some things you should ask them to consider. Number one, they don't know anything about a school of nursing and what it costs. Number two, you tell him you're not interested in a school unless they are interested in a school accredited by the National League of Nursing. Number three, you must insist that you have control over the admission policies, because at a state university they'll just take anybody. You can't have just anybody for a nurse. And, number four, you must be sure, before you start, that the State Board of Nursing isn't going to interfere with your program.' "

Miss Anderson says the school authorities were eager to accept the conditions Guy Hanner told her she should impose and she took the job.

Hanner's first wife had died in 1955. He married Loretta Anderson in 1957. She says, "Guy was generous, considerate, bright, dedicated to his job, and oh, so very tenacious. I thought when we were married — I was 42 and he was 72 — we might slow down, but it didn't work out that way." The poet Robert Browning says, "A man's reach should exceed his grasp, or what's a heaven for?" Guy Hanner was always reaching out to improve the quality of medical care in his adopted community. He died November 25, 1960, but he left the — his — hospital in good hands.

In 1945, the year Guy Hanner came to Good Samaritan, the hospital served 6,882 patients and there were 750 hospital births. In 1960, when he resigned, the hospital served 27,872 patients and there were 5,411 births. An additional 25,722 individuals received treatment in the Emergency Room.

One of the many improvements Guy Hanner made was in the Obstetrical Wing. Traditionally, newborns had been separated from their mothers for the first ten days or two weeks of their life. Hanner, at the urging of his Director of Nursing, Loretta Anderson, established what is called "rooming in." The babies were kept next to their mother's rooms and the mothers were encouraged to care for their babies almost from the moment of birth (a practice which is now universal).

Guy Hanner was largely responsible for the establishment of the Good Samaritan Auxiliary in 1953. The old Deaconess Hospital had benefited from the work of the "Women's Guild" from 1926 to 1930, when for some reason, unrecorded, the guild was disbanded.

Hanner enlisted Mrs. Richard (Benita) Fennemore and Mrs. B. F. C. (Barbara) Miller, who with Mrs. E. N. Holgate and Miss Loretta Coles organized the auxiliary on October 27, 1953. The first executive board included Mesdames Holgate, president; Shepard Hiscox, vice president; Hugh R. Meadows, second vice president; Frank Snell, constitution; Roy Tait, recording secretary; Edward Bringhurst, corresponding secretary; and M. Webster Stofer, treasurer.

When J. O. Sexson came to the Deaconess Hospital in 1923, the board of trustees were all Methodists and the institution was regarded in the community as exclusively Methodist. Sexson changed things gradually, including placing of representative members from other faiths on the board of trustees. When Hanner came it was truly an ecumenical group. Those original founders of the new auxiliary were leaders in the Episcopal, Roman Catholic, Methodist, Christian, and Baptist communions. By 1955 there were approximately 508 members of the auxiliary. Active members were required to donate a minimum of one hundred hours a year to the hospital. In their pink pinafores and white blouses the "pink ladies" operated a library for patients, helped in the Pediatric Department, were available to the Emergency Room outpatient clinics, and operated the hospital gift shop. The auxiliary commenced the sponsorship of "Candlelight Capers," a fund raising ball which is still held once each year. Since 1953 the auxiliary, through its fund raising efforts, has contributed substantially to improvements at Samaritan.

CHAPTER 9

The Explosive Decade

Between 1951 and 1960 the population of Phoenix increased 311 percent, from 106,118 to 429,170. The city limits were extended to 44th Avenue on the west, Cactus Road on the north, 32nd Street on the east to the Arizona Canal, then along the canal to the Scottsdale city limits. The southern boundary was the Salt River. This amazing growth was a result of new industries, more tourists, and the influx of more retirees. In that ten-year period, the population of Arizona increased 72 percent. The new people came because of the climate, the casual lifestyle, job opportunities, and the proliferation of refrigerated air conditioning.

Prodded by Gene Pulliam, publisher of *The Arizona Republic* and *The Phoenix Gazette*, Mayor Jack Williams and the Charter Government, City Council embarked on a planned program of annexation. The people living in the areas annexed wanted city services — sewers, fire and police protection. They wanted city zoning. They wanted to belong. They would no longer tolerate the old situation where, perhaps, one-half or two-thirds of the people who regarded Phoenix as their home had to live outside the city limits.

The people moved north and east, and then north and west. The industrial section between the railroad tracks and the Salt River held no attraction as a residential location. Some apartment houses were built, but most of the new construction was in single family residences — usually located on a good size lot where the owner could have his own private backyard, many of them with swimming pools.

A new type of retail establishment was being developed — the regional shopping center. Ralph Burgbacher, a California developer with vision, acquired the acreage once occupied by the Central Avenue Dairy just north of Thomas road, extending from Central to Third Avenue, where he constructed the Park Central shopping mall.

In the late 1940's, Goldwater's had acquired a square block between Moreland and Portland on Central, intending to construct a new store and move a little uptown from their former location. Instead, they moved to Park Central. Diamond's Boston Store, Porter's Men's Wear, and Vic Hanny joined the move.

Central Phoenix retail stores hung on by their fingernails, but the tide was irreversible. Downtown Phoenix would become a cluster of high rise central banking buildings, law offices, and downtown hotels. The city truly leapfrogged north, northwest, and northeast. There was nothing anyone could do, or would do, to stop it.

The other communities in the Salt River Valley — Mesa, Tempe, Scottsdale, and Glendale — enjoyed a similar pattern of growth.

Health care needs expanded as rapidly as the population growth. During the 1940's, one new hospital, St. Monica's, had been built through the inspiration of a Roman Catholic priest, Father Emmett McLoughlin, who located his institution in south Phoenix where service was desperately needed. Much of the funding came from the federal government.

In 1951, the Arizona Department of Health and Welfare licensed the Desert Mission Convalescent Hospital, later to be known as John C. Lincoln Hospital. This facility had 16 beds for inpatient care, a drug room, X-ray facilities, and an outpatient department, and was a beginning answer to desperate local need.

In 1907, retired architect W. R. Norton and his wife came to Arizona, homesteaded some land, and planned a subdivision to be called Sunnyslope. The location was nine miles north of the center of town, beyond the Arizona Canal, higher and drier than much of the rest of the Valley.

Sunnyslope became a haven for health seekers. They lived in shacks and tents in the Norton Tract, along Cave Creek Road and Dreamy Draw, at Hyatt's Camp (Cactus), and an area known as Erickson's Tract.

Most of the living quarters had dirt floors. The plight of the "lungers" was generally ignored by the people downtown.

As early as 1914 two ladies who lived in the area, Nancy Gould and Wilmina Phelps, began visiting the poor and the sick to do what they could to lessen the suffering.

In 1919 Mrs. W. A. Colley, her husband, and their asthmatic son arrived in Sunnyslope. Marguerite Colley was a practical nurse and a social worker. With Elizabeth Beatty, who came to the area in 1920, Marguerite Colley began soliciting help for the health seekers in the area. The Washington Women's Club and the Mission Circle of the First Presbyterian Church supported the effort and furnished turkey dinners at Christmas time and distributed gifts.

W. D. Himebaugh, a Sunday School missionary for the Presbyterian Synod of Arizona, established a Sunday School in Sunnyslope in 1925, with the help of Roy Bancroft, a singer and guitar player who had come to the desert to regain his health. Bancroft, a graduate of the Moody Bible Institute, became superintendent of that first Sunday School. The First Presbyterian Church in Phoenix assigned to the Reverend Joseph N. Hillhouse the task of developing the mission at Sunnyslope. Sarah McCahan, an active worker in the Second Presbyterian Church of Philadelphia, contributed $750, Clarence and Nancy Gould gave two lots, and a new chapel was constructed at a total cost of $1,500. It was completed on Labor Day, 1927.

Due to the efforts of the Reverend Mr. Hillhouse, a medical clinic was opened in 1929. Four Phoenix chest specialists, Doctors Fred Holmes, Howell Randolph, Victor Randolph and George Thorngate, gave generously of their time to treat the indigent ill.

When Cleveland industrialist John Cromwell Lincoln moved to Arizona in 1934 he and Mrs. Lincoln became interested in the missionary effort in Sunnyslope. Lincoln was active in supporting the YMCA. He became a member of the board of trustees of Good Samaritan Hospital. The Lincolns' gift of $2,000 to the Desert Mission, plus $1,000 contributed by Miss McCahan, provided the funds for the purchase for the Olney Tract, 20 acres of land between Dunlap and Hatcher, from Walnut (now Second Street) to Chestnut (now Third Street). The Lincolns made an additional contribution to finance the drilling of a water well on the property. In 1931 Desert Mission was reorganized as a Presbyterian Church.

By 1941 there were approximately 1,200 families living in the Sunnyslope area, and a building was constructed on the mission site to house convalescent patients. In 1942 a great fire destroyed most of the buildings. The United States was involved in World War II and no materials were available to rebuild. In 1947 a new clinic building was constructed as a result of a donation of $15,000 by contractor Roy Brooks.

In 1948 Herbert F. Hancox was appointed superintendent of the Desert Mission. In 1950 the Helen C. Lincoln Day Nursery was constructed with funds provided by Mrs. John C. Lincoln.

E. Ray Cowden, a prominent businessman and cattle rancher, came on the board of directors of the Desert Mission in 1946, and was elected president in 1949. Cowden and Herb Hancox were the leaders who developed this early facility into the John C. Lincoln Hospital. A new patient wing was constructed in 1955-56, at a cost of $200,000. John Lincoln and his wife contributed more than a quarter of that amount. When construction was completed the hospital had a total of 50 beds.

In 1953, St. Joseph's Hospital moved to a shining new $6 million facility at 350 West Thomas Road. St. Joseph's, founded by the Sisters of Mercy in 1895, and long considered one of the finest hospitals in the Southwest, enjoyed the affection of the community. The old quarters on North Fourth Street had been enlarged and remodeled until there was no more room for expansion. When the Sisters decided to move, the community responded. Industrialist Richard J. Cullen gave one-quarter million dollars for seed money. The medical staff matched his gift. The federal government contributed $1.5 million of Hill-Burton funds. Most of the rest was donated by grateful citizens.

St. Joseph's is just one of a system of hospitals operated and owned by the Sisters of Mercy, with headquarters in Burlingame, California. The system bestows many benefits on its member hospitals, including managerial skills, the experience of the other institutions, and procurement opportunities. The support of the Roman Catholic Church and the existence of the system mitigated the financial problems all hospitals encounter, and the people of Phoenix and Arizona have benefited.

Similarly, at Good Samaritan Hospital the '50s brought some dramatic changes, in the membership of the board of trustees and in administrative personnel, but there was no change in direction.

Colonel Lewis W. Coggins resigned from Samaritan's board in 1950 and died in 1953. This civic leader, who had pioneered the title business, was mayor of Phoenix, and the first non-Methodist asked to join the hospital's board of trustees, contributed his considerable talents to Good Samaritan for more than 30 years. A towering community figure since before the turn of the century, Coggins was a successful businessman, an avid sportsman, and a much better than average tennis player.

Most of the movers and shakers in the community from time to time could be found on the tennis court behind Colonel Coggins' home at 45 East Coronado, or over on the tennis court behind Dwight B. Heard's mansion on North Central.

The minutes of the hospital board reflect that Colonel Coggins missed very few meetings. Time and again the trustees made Coggins responsible for finding a solution to the vexing financial problems. During his years of service, he and J. O. Sexson are credited with enlisting the support of community leaders outside the Methodist Church.

Coggins was vice president of the board when Guy Alsap, Walter Wesley Knorpp, Ike Diamond, Moses B. Hazeltine of Prescott, and George Mickle came on board. He had been a strong supporter of K. S. Townsend's efforts to improve and enlarge the hospital's School of Nursing.

Other hard to replace members of the board died that year of 1950: attorney John Gust, member of the legal firm of Kibbey, Bennett, Gust and Smith; and banker Moses Hazeltine.

Under the vigorous administration of Guy Hanner, there was an almost continuous program of remodeling, upgrading, and improving of the physical plant. In 1951, it was decided to construct an entire new wing, one which would add 100 beds to the hospital capacity. The community was moving north. The new St. Joseph's was under construction. But the trustees of Good Samaritan did not even consider moving to a new location. The old-timers on the board were aware that if Good Sam moved, the existing plant and the land on which it was located would revert to the Methodist Church.

The buildings had an appraised value of more than one million dollars. Because of constant renovation, the physical facilities were equal to anything that could be provided in a brand new building. Unlike St. Joseph's, which had run out of land for expansion, Samaritan's goals had since the middle 1930's provided for expansion by acquiring new land adjacent to the hospital as it came on the market. A move was not indicated, but the increasing demand for health care prompted the construction of an entirely new five-story building to the west of the existing hospital. Before construction was completed, provision was made for adding a sixth floor.

J. O. Sexson was still active and maintained an office at the hospital, but the full load of administration fell on the shoulders of Guy Hanner. The board authorized Hanner to hire an administrative assistant and to make a place for an administrative resident.

Sexson had been drafted from the business world to rescue the Deaconess Hospital. He had no experience in hospital management. Hanner was a product of on-the-job training.

In the early 1940's Northwestern University, under the leadership of Malcolm McCreachron, M.D., was one of the first academic institutions to offer specific courses in hospital administration. By 1946, Northwestern, the University of Chicago, Columbia, Yale, Washington University, and St. Louis University were all offering graduate courses in hospital management.

Students seeking a master's degree in this specialized skill were required to complete one year of academic training and then serve one year of residency in an operating hospital, working under the close supervision of an acceptable preceptor. Hanner saw much promise in this, and Good Samaritan was the first hospital in Arizona to establish an administrative resident program.

Sexson had been the hospital's community front man — the joiner, the fund raiser, the business administrator. Hanner was more interested in the complicated inner workings of the hospital. He recognized the need for better education for both doctors and nurses. He understood the patients would be better cared for if the hospital climate was one of coordinated cooperation. He also recognized that new medical techniques, new procedures, new drugs, and new apparatus would rapidly and dramatically change the role of hospitals.

At Christmas time, 1952, Hanner and Sexson interviewed a young man from Arkansas who had made written application for the new position of administrative resident.

Stephen M. Morris was born on a farm in Denmark, Arkansas, the next to the youngest in a family of ten children. He had six older brothers, two older sisters, and one sister younger than he.

He says, "Farm families in those days were large because there was lots of work to do on the farm."

Immediately following graduation from high school in Searcy, Arkansas in 1946, he enlisted in the Navy and after training was assigned to a cruiser in the South Pacific.

World War II had ended in 1945, but all of Steve Morris' brothers had served in the military and it was something he wanted to do. When his tour of duty was finished, he enrolled at Arkansas College at Batesville. He says, "My mother had very little formal education, but she was determined that all her children should have the advantages she lacked. Six of us finished college, one earned a Ph.D. and three of us earned master's degrees."

With the outbreak of the Korean War, Morris was called back into service. By this time, thanks to the influence of one of his college classmates and the local Baptist pastor who served on the Arkansas Baptist Hospital board of trustees, he had decided to enter into hospital administration.

Morris volunteered for work in a service hospital and was assigned as a technician at the Fort Hood, Texas military hospital. When he was released from service, he completed his undergraduate work at Southwestern University in Georgetown, Texas, receiving his B.A. in Business Administration in June of 1952. He was admitted as a candidate for a master's degree in hospital administration by Washington University in St. Louis, and was in the middle of his academic year when he came to Phoenix to apply at Good Samaritan for the post of administrative resident. He chose Washington because the course was offered on the medical school campus in a hospital environment.

Morris says now that he almost did not come to Phoenix. "These interviews were scheduled during our Christmas vacation. I had been interviewed at Baptist Hospital in Memphis by Frank Groner, and he told me I could have the job. Euala and I (Morris had married Euala Crow, a school teacher, in Batesville, Arkansas, in 1949) had heard a lot about the Methodist Hospital in Houston, which now has a national reputation for its work in heart surgery. We drove to Houston. The administrator, Ted Bowen, was extremely warm and approving and said he would recommend me for the post in that institution. Phoenix was the third possibility. We had never been west, and to make the interview date we had in Phoenix it meant we would have to drive straight through. It is a long way from Houston, but we did it.

"I was impressed with both Good Samaritan Hospital and the Phoenix community," Morris says. "The westward tilt to the Sunbelt was just beginning. I decided Phoenix was going to grow and I wanted to grow with it. Good Samaritan was then only a 220-bed hospital, but I was impressed with what I saw. It compared favorably with both Houston and Memphis. And there was another consideration: Sexson was retired and Hanner was approaching retirement age. I had confidence in my ability to do the job and I thought I could probably stay on the administrative staff of either Memphis or Houston. But I had a feeling that for the long-range future my career had more potential in a growing situation such as Phoenix."

Morris says that was one time his hunch was right. In 1980, Frank Groner was still the administrator at Baptist Hospital in Memphis, Ted Bowen was still the administrator in Houston.

During his first year, Morris was involved in every phase of hospital activity — purchasing, supply, nursing administration, dietary kitchen, and surgical section. Vurlyne Boan, who was then assistant to the director of nursing at Good Samaritan, says, "Steve did everything. He was what we used to call a 'doughboy' in the service. He did all the things that no one else wanted to do. He solved a lot of problems for those of us who were on the staff. Guy Hanner was very fond of him and extremely pleased with the way he took hold."

In 1956 Stephen Morris was named an assistant administrator at Good Samaritan and when Guy Hanner retired in 1960, the trustees chose Morris to succeed Hanner. In the seven years which had elapsed, Good Samaritan had been increased in size from 220 to 440 beds. The pressures resulting from the community's 311 percent population growth had reached a boiling point.

In 1957 a citizen committee had recommended to the city a bond issue of $69,800,000. It was a tremendous sum of money, but the voters approved and the bond funds were used to improve the airport, streets, water supply, sewage plant, police and fire departments, library and parks. All of these improvements attracted additional newcomers and successive city councils have continued the struggle to meet the needs of the Valley's unprecedented population growth.

CHAPTER 10

Identified Unmet Needs

Improving city streets, adding to the airport, enlarging the sewage system, libraries, parks, police and fire protection were all municipal responsibilities. The bond issue proposed and passed by the Phoenix Growth Committee was an answer to the needs created by the increasing population.

In 1958 the Community Council, at the request of the Maricopa County Medical Society, sponsored a study of the health care needs and available resources in the metropolitan Phoenix area. The Council is the planning agency within the structure of the United Fund/Community Chest, private, charitable and service organizations. Valley Banker H. L. "Doc" Dunham, a leader in the solving of community problems, was responsible for the creation of the Community Council.

Membership was open to any individual or group interested in civic reform or improvement. Board members were elected. They represented business, labor, medicine, law, industry, the churches, the media (print and electronic), ethnic groups, health, welfare and cultural organizations.

The council has been described as the "conscience" of Phoenix. Earlier studies sponsored by this volunteer planning group resulted in improvements of the service offered by such diverse agencies as the YMCA and the Visiting Nurses.

When the Council decided to undertake a survey of the Valley's hospital needs, A. B. Schellenberg was president. Milt Graham, who was elected mayor of Phoenix later on, was vice president. None of the officers or members of the board of directors had any connection with any existing hospital.

The council named Walter E. Craig, who is now a federal judge, to serve as chairman of a citizen's advisory council to work in cooperation with James A. Hamilton Associates, a nationally acclaimed hospital consultant firm based at the University of Minnesota in Minneapolis.

Craig named 139 prominent community leaders to participate in this study. Thirty-two of these were doctors of medicine, representing the staffs of the existing hospitals and the county medical society. There was one dentist, one doctor of osteopathy. A smaller group, designated the "steering committee," with 52 members was named. There were 13 medical doctors in this group and two doctors of osteopathy.

The hospitals were represented by Emmett McLoughlin of Memorial, Sister Mary Placida of St. Joseph's, Guy Hanner of Good Samaritan, Herb Hancox of John C. Lincoln and W. J. Montignani of St. Luke's.

The hospitals were all struggling to meet the challenge of the new demands on health care. Individually and collectively, they were painfully aware of the revolutionary changes necessitated by the tremendous advances in the art of medical care, the introductions of new technologies and new procedures, and the bursting population in Central Arizona. They were, without exception, finding great difficulty in enlisting financial support adequate to the challenge. Each hospital had its own goals and enjoyed the strongly partisan support of its particular constituency.

The 156-page report by the citizens committee published in 1958 literally shocked the community into taking action. Among other things, the study predicted a dangerous shortage of hospital beds, said there had been an almost total lack of planning on a community-wide basis, predicted burdensome increases in the cost of hospital care, and said, "The complexities of modern medicine demand many expensive services which can prove unduly costly if they are spread out in too many hospitals vying for the same patient volume."

The report cautioned against overlapping and unnecessary duplication, and warned against the development of specialized hospital facilities.

The study said, "That even though hospitals may be physically separated, there are certain of their activities which can be coordinated and centralized, with a resulting economy of operations, savings in capital investment, and other benefits to the participating units without in any way impairing each hospital's autonomy."

As an example of coordinated activities, the study recommended centralized purchasing, bulk warehousing, a central laundry, a pooling of resources to support intern and resident physician programs.

Ignoring the origination and constituent individuality of the five hospitals, the report defined the broad responsibility and service area of the "central or district hospitals" having 350 or more beds; "community hospitals" with less than 350 beds. It also called for a program to serve the chronically ill and the geriatric patients.

In all, the report listed 65 general recommendations, including the construction of at least two new hospitals and enlargement and expansion at the existing hospitals.

It was a thoughtful, thoroughly documented report, designed to meet the future needs of a rapidly growing community. And it was the first in a series of studies supported by this representative community organization.

In ancient times, the Roman statesman Marcus Tullius Cicero observed that every great and good thing had within itself the seeds of its own destruction through an excess of its virtue. Modern critics phrase this observation somewhat differently, saying that the best motivated of reforms will often produce destructive, unintended consequences.

The unintended consequences of the Hamilton report actually resulted in the very thing the survey had warned against — a proliferation of hospitals, a duplication of services, and a drain on community resources.

The Hamilton report was a market survey. It spelled out future needs. It might be said this study emphasized the obvious. The five major hospitals had not been able to keep up with the community's growth.

Before the 1958 Hamilton study was published, community leaders outside the orbit of the five existing hospitals were taking steps to meet that unmet need. Four new hospitals were being planned: Phoenix Osteopathic on West Indian School Road, Doctors on East Thomas Road, Northwest in Glendale, and Maryvale.

In 1953 John F. Long, a resourceful developer, commenced the construction of an entirely new planned community west of the city limits, which he named Maryvale after his wife.

Long had grown up in Phoenix and served in the Army Air Corps during World War II. When the war was over he returned, married Mary Tolmachoff, and with borrowed money started to build a house for himself and his bride in 1946. He sold that house before it was completed, started two more, sold these, and from this small beginning developed one of the largest home building organizations in the Southwest.

Long employed a qualified community planner to help him lay out Maryvale. He provided land for schools, churches, parks, a golf course and a hospital.

In 1946 James and Katherine Chapman, both Doctors of Osteopathy, had opened a small hospital in Phoenix at 31 East McDowell Road. The facility had 30 beds. In 1953 a second osteopathic hospital was opened on North Seventh Street. The Doctors of Osteopathy involved in this venture were Richard McGill, Dwight Stiles, Sherman Meyer, J. Walter Larkin, Culmer Lucas, J. Robert Forbes, Franklin P. McCann, and Conde Call. Two years later, this organization took over the Chapmans' facilities on McDowell and, combined, were able to offer a total of 65 beds.

Operating two small hospitals in separate locations created serious problems for the management. In 1957 John R. Phillips, a local automobile dealer, proposed that a single new facility be constructed on slightly more than eight acres of ground at 1950 West Indian School Road, to be financed through the sale of callable bonds bearing an eight percent interest rate. Investor response was favorable because the rate of return was about twice that available at savings banks. Three hundred thousand dollars was raised and the new hospital, with 70 beds, was opened December 2, 1958.

Unlike the other "eight percenters," Phoenix Osteopathic had a history and a strong support from its constituency. In the 1940s and 1950s osteopathic medicine had gained substantial credibility. Courses in the osteopathic schools had been strengthened and graduates were required to have virtually the same training as graduates of other medical schools. Their training in manipulative treatment was an add-on to the regular curriculum of medicine and surgery. In 1959 Phoenix Osteopathic expanded from 60 to 108 beds.

At about the same time this first bond sale was taking place, the Universal Development Corporation of California, a private investment firm, entered the picture. They approached two highly respected members of the medical community with extensive practices on the west side of town, Doctors William E. McGee and Phillip Rice, with an offer to build a new hospital in the Maryvale community. The institution was to be financed with eight percent bonds. The total cost was estimated to be $4,400,000. John F. Long provided land located at 51st Avenue and Campbell, the bonds were sold, and construction was commenced. Northwest Hospital, a 60-bed facility located at 6010 West Northern Avenue in Glendale, also financed by the sale of eight percent bonds, was opened in 1960.

Doctor J. Allen Ginn established a proprietary hospital on East Thomas Road. Ginn and some of his close associates in the medical field provided the funds, and the new institution was called Doctors Hospital.

Even with these additions — 108 beds at Phoenix Osteopathic (now called Phoenix General), 144 beds at Maryvale, 60 beds at Northwest, and 99 beds at Doctors — the problems outlined in the Hamilton survey were unanswered. There was no local, state or federal law regulating the construction of new hospitals. Thus, there was no way the local community, either through the Council or any other voluntary and governmental entity, could prevent the subsequent misapplication of the excellent recommendations of the Hamilton report.

Phoenix General, Maryvale, and Northwest were not-for-profit community organizations. The out-of-state promoters who provided the financing for Maryvale and Northwest earned substantial commissions on the sale of the bonds, walked away, and left the local management with the responsibility for repaying the borrowed money.

James D. Jennings, president of Summit Construction Company, sold eight percent bonds to finance two new hospitals, Phoenix Children's Hospital (now Phoenix Baptist) at 6025 North 20th Avenue, and Scottsdale City Hospital (now Scottsdale Memorial), in that growing northeast Valley community.

Another hospital was built by the "eight percenters" in Mesa and is now known as Mesa Lutheran.

During this period there were some substantial changes on the Good Samaritan board. J. O. Sexson died of a heart attack while attending the Methodist Conference at Redlands, California, and vice president Mac Best was moved up to take Sexson's place. Of that original group, only Dr. J. C. Norton was left. He had been a member of the hospital board for more than 40 years. He died in 1954, the same year that B. F. Youngker, a successful agriculturist from the Buckeye area, was named to the board of trustees. The capacity of the hospital was just about doubled, from 220 to 440 beds, with the completion of a new six-story West Wing.

In 1956 hospital employees, who had been working a 48-hour week for very modest wages, had their pay increased and the work week shortened to 40 hours. Minutes of the board of trustees reflect this change was unavoidable. The wage scale in California for nurses, technicians, orderlies, and general hospital help was substantially higher than rates in Phoenix. The nurses in California had organized and won a reduction from the 48-hour to the 40-hour week in the early 1950s. And while the Good Samaritan School of Nursing continued to graduate competent nurses, a great many of them took their diplomas and went to greener pastures.

Good Samaritan was enjoying near-capacity utilization, averaging almost 90 percent, but there was a constant demand for new and improved services. A group of doctors, including Dermont Melick, A. R. Grant, Edward Bregman, Daniel Cloud, Wallace Reed, Joe Ehrlich, Frederic Becker, Robert Phillips, Lee Ehrlich and James D. Barger, persuaded the hospital management to establish a cardio-pulmonary laboratory for congenital, as well as acquired, heart diseases.

CHAPTER 11

Who–When–Why

The separation of church and state called for by the Founding Fathers in the First Amendment, "Congress shall make no law respecting an establishment of religion or prohibiting the free exercise thereof...," has over the years produced much learned argument. Prayer has been banned in the public schools, but religious principles, both Christian and Jewish, guided the founding of our Republic.

Those ringing words in the Declaration of Independence, "We hold these truths to be self evident, that all men are created equal, that they are endowed by their Creator with certain unalienable rights," have shaped the American ethos. We have abided by the instruction to preach, to teach, and to heal.

Our churches, our educational institutions, and our hospitals represent society's response. The great teaching hospitals and the first universities were sponsored by religious bodies, organized not for profit, but to serve a charitable need. Nowhere is this more evident than in the history of the hospitals created first in the Territory and then in the State of Arizona. The Methodist, Episcopalian, Presbyterian, Baptist and the Roman Catholic communions have played the major roles. Their efforts have been supported by the communities they serve. In organizational structure they are all remarkably similar, with responsibility for management vested in a governing body of community minded individuals. Without exception, their purpose has been to provide a high quality of medical care for all sorts and conditions of men, regardless of race, creed, color, or economic status.

Of necessity, these governing bodies have been self-perpetuating. But the properties they administer are held in trust for the community and belong to the community. They are volunteers, serving without pay in the service of all humanity. The men and women who have acted as custodians of these public trusts have given countless thousands of hours to the development of a health care system in the United States of America which has outdistanced that of any other nation on Earth. Our resources have been augmented by the operation of tax-supported hospitals, receiving funds from the federal government, cities, counties, and states, and, in recent years, by institutions owned by investors and operated for profit.

All hospitals, those operated by the government, by for-profit corporations and not-for-profit, must answer to a number of diverse clienteles.

Doctors demand the hospitals in which they work provide the very latest in technology. These new devices for diagnosis and treatment are extremely expensive. A machine for computerized axial tomography costs more than $1 million. A linear accelerator, essential to the treatment of some types of cancer, may cost as much as $2 million. The latest diagnostic device, called the Nuclear Magnetic Resonance system, carries a price tag of $2 million. X-ray equipment, monitoring devices for intensive care units, and sophisticated laboratory apparatus, all levy an increased demand on the hospital's capital resources.

Doctors, who must be constantly aware of the possibility of malpractice suits in our litigious society, want the supporting service of the best pathologists the hospital can find, and the most prestigious roentgenologists. Hospital administrators and their boards are, therefore, under constant pressure from their medical staffs to acquire the most up-to-date medical equipment. Since physicians (not patients) are the "first" clientele of the hospital and since physician dissatisfaction can readily be translated into loss of patients, hospitals have difficulty in resisting physician demand for new medical technology, even though such costly equipment may be under-utilized or duplicate similar resources in nearby institutions.

It is this "reality" which was examined, in part, by the Hamilton study and which led to the several recommendations toward joint planning and joint programming by several facilities.

No one ever really wants to go to a hospital. The decision is forced by circumstance; the ill and the injured have no other choice. Hospitalization is painful, expensive and risky. Advances in medical science have greatly minimized the risk. Patients with diseases once considered fatal can now be cured or, if not fully cured, restored to a point where they can lead happy, useful lives. Heart surgery is commonplace. Patients confronted with renal failure can now survive for great lengths of time on kidney dialysis. Chemotherapy and radiation, together with new surgical techniques, have lengthened the life span of hundreds of thousands of cancer sufferers. But the decision to seek treatment, to go to the hospital, is always a forced one.

The welfare of the patient must be the first concern of every hospital. But the patient's doctor is in complete control. The doctor selects the hospital, admits the patient, orders the treatment, determines the length of stay, and then discharges the patient. The hospital must serve both clients — the doctor and the patient. The medical staff is a fiercely independent group of private physicians. If the hospital fails to provide the latest in medical apparatus, the best pathological and radiology service, the doctors will take their patients elsewhere.

It is the responsibility of hospital management to attempt to distribute equably the costs of maintaining all these sophisticated devices and services, which may actually be needed by no more than a quarter of the patients admitted. But no hospital administrator or doctor can predict with any degree of certainty when the patient may suddenly encounter a life-threatening situation and require one or more of these extremely expensive diagnostic or therapeutic services.

In the past 30 years, a third clientele has entered the picture — the third party payer: insurance companies, employers who provide health care to their employees as a fringe benefit, and the largest of them all, the federal government, with Medicare and Medicaid. The unintended consequences of this insertion of a third clientele has resulted in over-utilization of some facilities. The patient who knows that someone else is going to pay the bill has no incentive to question the cost of that service. As a direct result of the improvement in medical techniques and the entrance of the third party payer, the cost of medical care has escalated dramatically. Twenty years ago as a society we spent about five percent of our gross income on health care. Today that figure is more than ten percent.

Twenty years ago the patient with an ailing hip was advised to buy a cane and take some aspirin. Today the orthopedic surgeons can give the patient an entire new hip, but at a cost of about $10,000. We can transplant livers, and kidneys, and hearts, delay death with life-support systems, all of which has created tremendous ethical and financial problems for the medical community and the hospitals.

All of these problems were first brought to the attention of the residents of metropolitan Phoenix with the publication of the Hamilton Survey.

When Stephen M. Morris was named administrator of Good Samaritan Hospital, Harold Divelbess was president of the board of trustees; Richard Lewis was vice president; B. F. McGough, secretary, and E. W. Montgomery, treasurer. Other members of the board were Del Drinen, Harold Diamond, Sherman Hazeltine, Dave Heywood, John Kerr, Walter Lucking, A. W. Miller, Frank Snell, Benny Carter, L. J. Taylor, B. F. Youngker, and Wes Knorpp.

Divelbess was named to the board when his law partner, John Gust, died. Dick Lewis was president and general manager of KTAR Radio and T.V. Sherman Hazeltine was president of the First National Bank of Arizona. His father had first joined the board of trustees in 1928. Heywood was a prominent Mormon. Walter Lucking was president of Arizona Public Service. Frank Snell, who had been named to the board after the death of J. O. Sexson, was a senior partner in the prestigious law firm of Snell and Wilmer. L. J. Taylor was associated with Phoenix Title and Trust. B. F. Youngker was a successful farmer from the Buckeye area. John Kerr was the local manager for the E. F. Woolworth Company, and Knorpp, the former publisher of the *Republic and Gazette*.

McGough had been on the board since 1931. All of these men were truly representative of the community, were serious about their responsibilities as trustees of the hospital, and were active in other community affairs.

Morris says, "We had problems. Despite the opening of new hospitals, there was a severe shortage of beds. In 1950 we had admitted about 10,000-plus patients. In 1960 we admitted 27,872 patients. Between the time I came here as a administrative resident in 1953 and the day I was named administrator, we had increased our bed capacity from 220 to 440. We doubled in size but the patient load had increased almost 200 percent. We had opened a new heart clinic in September, 1958, which in its first year took care of 47 seriously ill patients.

"Medical education, the intern and resident programs, and the School of Nursing were costing us about $200,000 a year. The Outpatient Department, which was opened in 1951, was providing service for almost 22,000, and about the same number received care in the Emergency Room. "When the hospital opened on McDowell Road in 1923, there were thirty physicians with staff privileges. By 1960 there were almost 500. The Maricopa Hospital Development Corporation, which had launched a drive for $8 million following the release of the Hamilton study, produced some very welcome funds, but not nearly enough to do what needed to be done.

"The board of trustees was a working board. We met every month, there was always some needed repair which had to be considered, and these businessmen reviewed every contract. Labor costs amounted to more than 60 percent of our budget and, even though revenues had increased, they didn't quite keep pace with the increase in operating costs. Frequently the board meetings lasted from 3:30 in the afternoon to well past midnight, with only a break for a quick snack.

"Every member of the board made it plain to me I could call on them for advice and counsel at any time, and that is what I did. If it was a legal matter, I went to Harold Divelbess or Frank Snell. I don't know what their hourly rate was at that time, but they gave me and the hospital hundreds of hours of advice free. Wes Knorpp had a wonderful understanding of the community. I relied on him particularly when we had personnel problems. If it was financial I talked to Sherm Hazeltine or Harold Diamond. John Kerr probably had a better understanding of future possibilities. He wanted us to build a branch hospital on some land we owned on Camelback Road, but the board didn't think it feasible at the time. We were always having problems with the hospital's wells. At that time, every building in town had its own well. The water was taken from the underground at a temperature of 70 or 75 degrees, used to cool the refrigerant gases, and then returned to the underground in a separate well. Bennie Youngker had drilled hundreds of wells in the Buckeye area, and if it was a drilling or pump problem, I went to Bennie and he would solve it for me. Lewis Taylor was the historian. If I was searching for a precedent or to find out past policy, I went to him. Vinson and Carter were leading electrical contractors; if we had construction problems or needed mechanical repairs, I could get some common sense advice from Ben Carter. I had good rapport with all the board members. When I was criticized for some action or some statement, they generally supported me.

"When all those eight percent bond hospitals were started in the late '50s, I told the press that, in my opinion, it was the wrong way to finance hospital construction. I said the promoters would walk off with the profits and the hospitals were certain to run into financial difficulties. I remember one time a man from Minnesota came down and asked me if he could buy some eight percent bonds from our hospital. I told him we could borrow the money we needed from the bank at four percent and that we would never go the bond route. My remarks offended some of the doctors and community leaders who were pinning all their hopes on these new eight percent bond institutions. Some of the members of the Samaritan board of trustees were asked to 'put a muzzle on Steve Morris.' They didn't. In time all of the eight percenters, with the exception of Osteopathic (which is now called Phoenix General), did run into trouble."

The Community Council, which had been responsible for that first James A. Hamilton survey of health needs, did not let the matter drop. In 1961 Edward "Bud" Jacobson, president of the Council, with the support of Doc Dunham and the Council board of directors, enlisted more than 355 volunteer citizens to participate in an exhaustive study and evaluation of the health services available to Phoenix. They divided into ten task forces, or subcommittees, to examine history and resources, maternal and child health and school health, infectious diseases, adult health and rehabilitation, agency evaluation, mental health, environmental health, health of the migrant, and financing. The results of their efforts were printed in a 191-page booklet on June 1, 1962. Working under the guidance of H. D. Chope, M.D., director of the San Mateo County California Health and Welfare Department, with a staff supervised by Community Council Executive Director Milton Gan, they documented Phoenix's future needs and evaluated the current response to those needs.

Names make tedious reading and almost 22 years have passed since that survey was published, but the names of that Council's board of directors, even at this late date, clearly indicate the quality and credibility of their findings. In addition to H. L. Dunham, Vice President of the Valley National Bank who was Honorary Life President of the Council, others on the board of directors were: President "Bud" Jacobson, partner in the law firm of Snell and Wilmer and active in the community's art, theater and music entities; Jack Williams, Mayor of Phoenix and later governor of the state; Mrs. John Eisenbeiss, wife of a prominent neurosurgeon and on the board of the Child Guidance Clinic; Mrs. Joseph Clifford, president of Family Service and active Republican party fund raiser; Robert B. Roe, Manager, Sperry-Phoenix; Mrs. Monroe Blakely, member of the board of Florence Crittenton Home and wife of a major oil dealer in the area; W. Albert Brewer, M.D., past president of the county medical society; George C. Bright, Manager, Penn-Mutual Life Insurance Company; James Byers, 1st Vice President, First National Bank of Arizona; Tom Chauncey, owner, KOOL Television; J. P. Clemons, President, Arizona Title and Trust Company; Reverend John Doran, pastor, St. Thomas Aquinas Catholic Church and editor, local Catholic newspaper; Stan Farnsworth, M.D., county health officer; Ed Fitzhugh, editor, *The Phoenix Gazette*; Ben P. Frissell, internist and officer of the county medical society; Mrs. John S. Kruglick, active in Salvation Army and later member of the Phoenix City Council; Bernard G. LeBeau, officer, Arizona Bank; John L. Liecty, Treasurer, Arizona Public Service Company; Mrs. T. E. (Nada) Peterson, Jr., officer, Junior League; W. A. Robinson, retired principal of Carver School, first "integrated" school in Phoenix; Reverend George R. Selway, D.D., Dean, Episcopal Cathedral; J. William Sweeney, Certified Public Accountant; Dr. Arnold Tilden, Dean, School of Liberal Arts, Arizona State University; and J. Charles Wetzler, owner of Circle One Livestock Company and active leader in the agricultural and cattle industries.

The hospital section of that Community Council report begins with this statement, "In addition to offering purely curative care, the hospital has developed into a basic institution providing technical facilities for health appraisal, diagnosis, and treatment of disease, and an indispensable workshop for the practitioner. Through its ability to make modern procedures available, the hospital exercises a strong influence on the quality and quantity of medical service. The impact of scientific advances, the changing methods of medical education and patterns of medical practice, and the modern treatment of diseases, including chemotherapy and early ambulation, have accelerated the *obsolescence* of hospital equipment and physical plants."

At the time of the report there were four federal hospitals in Maricopa County, three state, one county, 15 charity or community, and two classified as proprietary.

There were, according to the survey, just slightly more than 1,800 suitable beds available to the residents of Maricopa County in 1961. The smaller hospitals were under-utilized, the larger hospitals were overcrowded. The conclusion, "If no new beds were built, the shortage in 1965 would be: acute general 882, chronic active treatment 336, psychiatric non-custodial 281, tuberculosis 487."

This citizen study classified hospitals as (1), the district hospital, which would provide all the bed services available in a smaller hospital, augmented by beds for the care of the various medical and surgical specialties. The facilities necessary to care for the highest degree of complicated illness should be concentrated in the district hospital, in order to insure the most effective utilization of the highly skilled professional personnel and the expensive technical equipment necessary for such care. The report says, "With the district hospital will rest the primary responsibility for the educating of medical, nursing, and technical personnel, not only for the local area but for an extensive surrounding region as well. These hospitals should provide intern and resident physician training in the four basic services, in the various medical and surgical specialties, and in the ancillary services of anesthesiology, pathology, and radiology."

The community hospital (2), according to the survey, would provide general care beds for the basic services of general medicine and surgery, obstetrics and pediatrics. They should only increase in size and scope in response to an increase in the population they serve. "The community hospital should avoid the provision of facilities for certain complicated procedures involving unusual capital investment and operating costs where facilities are already in existence in larger district hospitals."

These concerned citizens also called for facilities to serve the chronically ill (3) and geriatric patients (4).

JAMES OSCAR SEXSON
Administrator, Good Samaritan Hospital,
from 1924-1948.

MRS. J. O. (EDITH) SEXSON

GOOD SAMARITAN HOSPITAL
In the 1930's.

DR. PAUL JARRETT

DR. L. D. BECK

DR. WILLIAM O. SWEEK

DR. E. HENRY RUNNING

DR. CARLOS CRAIG

DR. DERMONT W. MELICK

DR. J. GORDON SHACKELFORD
Dentist and oral surgeon appointed to the staff
of Good Samaritan Hospital in 1923.

JOHN GUST

M. O. "MAC" BEST
Long-time members of Good Samaritan's
board of trustees.

E.W. MONTGOMERY

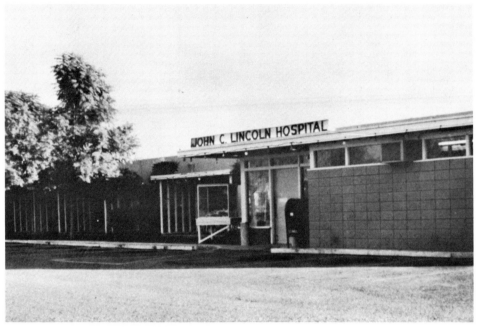

ORIGINAL JOHN C. LINCOLN HOSPITAL

JOHN C. LINCOLN
Prominent Cleveland industrialist who came to Arizona in the early '30's, served on the board of trustees of Good Samaritan Hospital and, with his wife, was the principle benefactor of the John C. Lincoln Hospital.

HERB HANCOX
Administrator, John C. Lincoln Hospital.

GUY M. HANNER
Administrator, Good Samaritan Hospital, 1948-1960. He carried on the tradition of services established by J. O. Sexson.

FRANK SNELL
Long-time member of the board of trustees, Good Samaritan Hospital.

DR. PAUL L. SINGER
Still active in the affairs of the Samaritan Hospital system.

STEPHEN M. MORRIS
Who came to Good Samaritan as an Administrative Resident in 1952.

WALTER R. BIMSON
Under his leadership the Valley Bank contributed substantially to the growth of the Salt River Valley.

PHOENIX MAYOR JACK WILLIAMS
Who served as Governor, 1967-1975.

EUGENE C. PULLIAM
Publisher of *The Arizona Republic/The Phoenix Gazette,* 1946-1975 — a leader in the cultural and economic growth of the Salt River Valley.

U.S. SENATOR BARRY M. GOLDWATER

MRS. B.F.C. (BARBS) MILLER WITH HER HUSBAND, "BEANIE"
Barbs was one of the founders of the Good Samaritan Auxiliary.

MRS. E. N. (IZZIE) HOLGATE and MRS. RICHARD (BENITA) FENNEMORE
Two of the founders of the Good Samaritan Auxiliary.

ALLEN ROSENBERG
Community leader. A leader in the group which led to the establishment of the Phoenix Children's Hospital at Good Samaritan Medical Center.

E. RAY COWDEN
Businessman, community leader who helped develop the John C. Lincoln Medical Center.

GOOD SAMARITAN HOSPITAL, 1980

LOIS GRUNOW CLINIC
The first medical office building constructed adjacent to the Good Samaritan Hospital.
　　　　—Stephen Shadegg

Obvious deficiencies were noted. Arizona had no mandatory milk pasteurization law, no requirement that raw milk should be so labeled when sold in stores and restaurants. There was no licensing or regulation of laboratories which provided physicians with analysis of blood, body chemistry, x-rays; no provision for inspection of locally killed poultry or meat; no regulation of nursing homes. Only four out of 45 nursing homes examined had registered nurses in their employ. The problem of increased air pollution is noted, along with overtaxed sewage treatment plants. In that year, only half the public swimming pools were examined to determine the bacteriological and chemical content of the water. The incidence of tuberculosis in Arizona was 80 percent greater than the national average, and the infant death rate in Maricopa County higher than the national average. The report covers the health care aspect of social service agencies and the Maricopa County Hospital. It emphasizes the need for continuing medical education, psychiatric and psychological counselling, home care, and central planning.

The reporters examined the cost of medical care, predicted that it would increase, and called for community response to improve the quality, the quantity, the availability of health care, and the adoption of some cost containment strategy.

It was all there, all the data in one comprehensive report, but the growing Phoenix community had other things on its mind. There was rapid expansion to the north and northwest along the Black Canyon Freeway. ChrisTown, billed as the largest completely covered shopping mall in the world, was opened in August of 1961.

Attorney Joe Ralston, former president of the Community Council and John Clements of Phoenix Title and Trust, with a half dozen concerned citizens supporting their effort, converted the Hospital Development Corporation into a planning council for hospitals. They changed the name to Health Facilities Planning Council.

In the summer of 1966, James D. Jennings, who had promoted two eight percent bond hospitals in the early '60s, made public his plan to construct an 86-bed hospital at the corner of 67th Avenue and Bethany Home Road. He proposed to finance the facility through the sale of $1,987,000 worth of eight percent bonds. He said the new north Phoenix institution would serve the osteopathic community.

The Health Facilities Planning Council, which had been struggling to coordinate the expansion of health facilities in accordance with the Community Council's study proposals, issued a public statement condemning the proposal.

The Arizona Osteopathic Medical Association said that no member of their association was associated with this new promotion.

The Planning Council said the promoters were misleading the public by claiming new beds were needed in the proposed location and asked the Office of Securities and Exchange Commission to investigate the legitimacy of the offering.

Articles in the Phoenix newspapers reviewed the performance records of the five hospitals which had been originally financed through the sale of eight percent bonds. The paper said Phoenix Osteopathic, under its new name, Phoenix General, had paid off principal and interest within ten years. Maryvale had been forced into reorganization under Chapter 10 of the federal bankruptcy laws, had defaulted on its interest payments the first year, and was operating under the supervision of the federal court and a trustee. Phoenix Children's, promoted by Jennings, had gone into receivership and was taken over by the Arizona Southern Baptist Convention. Scottsdale City, another Jennings promotion, unable to meet its interest payments, had been rescued by the Baptist Hospital. The newspapers said neither Jennings nor Stovall, the spokesman for the proposed new hospital, could be located. As a result of the vigorous action by the Health Facilities Planning Council and the resulting publicity, the promoters abandoned their efforts.

In 1966 the name of the Health Facilities Planning Council was changed to the Comprehensive Health Planning Council. The parent organization received fifty percent of its funding from the federal government, which mandated that the local boards be made up of one-third hospital administrators, one-third physicians, and one-third board members of hospitals. The new federal legislation, titled the Comprehensive Health Planning Act (PL 89-749), did away with the old board structure and required only that a majority of the board must be consumers. Milton Gan, who had been executive secretary of the Community Council at the time of the Hamilton survey and the follow-up study, was named executive director in 1968.

Gan says, "The early Health Facilities Planning Council had directed its attention only to facilities and capital costs. The new federal legislation expanded the responsibilities of the Comprehensive Health Planning Council to include health care facilities other than hospitals.

In 1974 the federal legislation was again amended (PL 93-641). Among other things, the new law required the governors to divide their states into geographical areas described as "Health Service Areas." Arizona was divided into five such regions. The law specified that each of these areas contain a health planning agency, called Health Systems Agency. This new creation was to be governed by a board of 30 persons selected in such a manner that they would have to mirror the social, economic, ethnic, racial, sex, age, geographical subdivisions and professional health interests of the area.

Twelve to 14 members were to be health providers. Sixteen to 18 members were to be consumers.

Under the statute a provider could be any person who earned ten percent or more of his income from the health care industry which included insurance, teaching, selling of health care products as well as doctors, nurses, hospital administrators, etc.

There was to be a "Statewide Health Coordinating Council" structured in a similar manner to the boards of the local Health Systems Agencies and a "State Health Planning and Development Agency."

The requirement that the boards reflect the socio-economic and other aspects of the population has been described by many observers, including Milton Gan, as the most disastrous provision of the new law.

Gan says, "While conceptually interesting, it removed the community's power structure from the local health planning organization.

"With the implementation of the 1974 federal health planning law, the agency's influence was diminished rather than enhanced. The most competent, experienced, capable, knowledgeable, dedicated, and influential citizens were no longer permitted to participate on the board of the local health planning body."

Commenting on the results of the implementation of this new law, Gan contrasts the accomplishment of the Community Council studies with the work of the newly created Central Arizona Health Systems Agency.

"The Community Council utilized the insights and knowledge of health professional groups on study committees, but it reserved its policy-making powers to citizens who had proven civic, business, economic or other broad-based interests in the community's well-being.

"By contrast, the policy-making powers of the Health Systems Agencies was formulated by persons who, in the main, had no such community-wide responsibilities or experience, or by persons whose primary purpose on the board was to protect their own special health service corporation."

Gan, who has been described by former Mayor/former Governor Jack Williams as a brilliant and devoted administrator, remained with the CAHSA until the Arizona Legislature passed a "sunset" law to phase out the agency by 1984.

CHAPTER 12

Expansion and Modernization

The Hamilton report and the Community Council study focused public attention exclusively on the deficiencies and inadequacies of the community's health care delivery system. Nowhere in either report is there the slightest recognition of the very remarkable improvement in both quality and quantity achieved in this decade of the '50s by the individual hospitals, the medical community and certain cooperative governmental agencies.

Effective treatment of tuberculosis was no longer dependent upon long periods of bed rest and exposure to the open air. Surgical procedures — collapse therapy — widely recommended in the '30s and '40s, were giving way to new drugs. The St. Luke's board of trustees, with the support of the Right Reverend Arthur Barksdale Kinsolving, II, Bishop of the Episcopal Diocese of Arizona, moved to take on new responsibilities. With the aid of some federal funding, a new building was constructed to serve more as a general hospital than a tuberculosis sanitarium.

St. Luke's has grown and changed to meet the community needs. When Atwood raised the original funds to open St. Luke's Home, Arizona was a Missionary District of the Episcopal Church. The title to the small tubercular sanitorium was vested in a corporation governed by a board of directors, "a majority of whom shall be adherents to the Protestant Episcopal Church." Bert Cocks, the first superintendent, was an ordained Episcopal priest. Most of those early patients had some church connection. The Episcopal Bishop of Arizona was traditionally president of the board of directors.

In the late '40s this requirement was dropped to permit the hospital to attract to its board non-Episcopalians. The Bishop of Arizona became an ex officio member of that board. In February, 1950, the name was changed to St. Luke's Hospital.

In 1972 St. Luke's bought the Franklin Hospital, a small treatment center for alcoholics, and moved the operation to the campus on 18th Street. Brian Lockwood, who became administrator at St. Luke's in 1969, believes the evolution of the institution to a specialty hospital was a natural progression. He says, "We never offered pediatrics or obstetrics. What we have now on campus is St. Luke's Hospital, a 280-bed medical/surgical hospital with its own board. Then we have St. Luke's Behavioral Health Center, which is a 150-bed psychiatric hospital. And we are now in the process of building the Harrington Arthritis Research Center. The parent corporation for these three entities is St. Luke's Medical Center."

In 1981 Lockwood helped organize Combined Health Resources, a management group, to operate St. Luke's, acquire other institutions and establish a close affiliation with other community hospitals.

Combined Health Resources purchased the long-established 100-bed Adventist Hospital in Tempe. Combined Health Resources established a close affiliation with Chandler Community Hospital, which has been enlarged and modernized to accommodate 120 beds. Another affiliate, the Homako Hospital in Casa Grande, will complete a new 100-bed building in July of 1984 and be renamed Casa Grande Regional Medical Center. A small hospital in Parker, Arizona is also affiliated with Combined Health Resources.

Lockwood believes the system approach will provide the public with high quality medical care at the lowest possible cost. He regrets the fact that the relationship between the Episcopal Church and St. Luke's has been weakened over the years and says he would like to see increased diocesan participation. "I think one of the things we have to bring to the health care system is our values. Regardless of what church you believe in, values are very important to health care."

The churches of America were responsible for the establishment of many of the institutions we cherish today. The first universities, the first hospitals, were church inspired and church supported. Alexis de Tocqueville commented on the religious strength supporting the character of the people of America, and the four great hospitals in Central Arizona — St. Joe's, St. Luke's, Good Sam and John C. Lincoln — were all originally church-sponsored institutions. With the exception of St. Joseph's, they are not today. But, as Brian Lockwood put it, "values" are still important to our society.

The changes which have occurred in the practice of medicine and in the role of the community hospitals have occurred gradually. Dr. Dermont W. Melick, who was in active practice in Arizona between 1956 and 1982, was in a position where he could both observe and participate in the changes.

Melick, whose father, grandfather, and great-grandfather were all doctors, was born in Williams. His father, Dr. Prince Albert Melick, built that town's first hospital in 1898. Melick was 21 years old when he was graduated from the University of Arizona and only 25 when he was graduated from the University of Pennsylvania Medical School. He then served a two-year internship, returned to Williams, and entered general practice. After 14 months of small town medicine, he left to pursue post-graduate studies at the University of Pennsylvania and then to a three-year residency in thoracic surgery at the University of Wisconsin. He moved to Phoenix, was accepted as a member of the staff at Good Samaritan in 1945, and nine years later was chosen chief of staff.

When Arizona's first medical school was opened in Tucson in 1967, Melick left private practice to accept appointment as Professor of Surgery and Director of the Arizona Regional Medical Program.

Melick, who spent his childhood in the environment of the small one-man hospital where his mother was business manager, cook, janitor, bill collector and nurse, was particularly sensitive to the changing role of the hospital as provider of medical care.

"Until about the middle '50s," Melick says, "there were no professional hospital administrators. The doctors dominated. With the advent of trained administrators, the intrusion of government and third-party payers, this has changed. There is still some tension between the administrators and the medical staff, but gradually a new atmosphere of cooperation is developing." From the very beginning the principle of peer review was implicit in the organization of the hospital staffs. When the hospitals were small, the doctors all knew each other, and the procedures were still fairly simple, very little supervision was required. As the hospitals and the medical staffs expanded, and the age of specialties emerged, peer review became essential. No longer are physicians granted unlimited privileges by the hospitals. More often than not they are limited to specific areas and their work is subject to supervision by practitioners established in that field. Without question, this practice improves protection for the patient, but it has led to difficulties within the medical-hospital community. Doctors whose skills are below average or tend to be "knife happy" resent the restrictions imposed by the modern hospital administrations, but the patient is the beneficiary. Fewer unnecessary procedures are performed and the general quality of health care in the hospital has been materially improved.

Melick says, "When I came on the staff at Good Samaritan, the rooms, hallways, surgical and laboratory facilities were all painted a sort of dingy off-white. The businessmen on the board were just that, businessmen. They didn't want the doctors running their hospital and we couldn't blame them for that. The professionally trained hospital administrators who emerged in the '50s had a combination of skills and understandings. They were trained in business administration, but they were also trained to appreciate the particular responsibilities of the hospital. Or to put it another way, they knew the difference between a hotel, where guests receive room and board, and a hospital, where surgery and medicine and care can restore the health and give new hope to the patients."

Melick performed the first open heart surgery in Arizona at Good Samaritan on Johnny Young, a six-year-old boy, in June of 1947. On his way to the grocery store carrying an empty glass milk bottle, the little boy had fallen. The bottle shattered and a sharp-pointed fragment penetrated the left anterior-precordial area. Melick opened the chest cavity, sutured the wound, the boy recovered, and medical history was made. Although the patient always had an abnormal electrocardiogram, he lived a normal life for 30 years, was accepted for service in the U.S. Marines, and died as a result of an automobile accident.

In this same decade of the '50s, John C. Lincoln Hospital was expanded, St. Joseph's moved to new and larger quarters, the eight percenters were constructed, and Good Samaritan's capacity was more than doubled.

On January 14, 1961, on land adjacent to the new St. Joseph's Hospital, ground was broken for the construction of the Barrow

Neurological Institute. A five-story modern structure with 50-beds, it was constructed for treatment of diseases of the brain and spinal cord and to provide facilities for basic research into the normal and abnormal functioning of the nervous system. This great addition to the medical resources of the community became possible when Charles A. Barrow of Litchfield Park offered to contribute half a million dollars towards the construction of the institute if the hospital would raise a like amount.

Barrow's wife, Julia, had suffered from a neurological ailment over a period of 17 years. When the hospital had difficulty raising its share of the needed money, the Barrow family contributed an additional half million dollars, plus another $120,000 for various laboratories and a seizure clinic. The Barrow Neurological Institute and its medical director, neurologist John Raymond Green, are recognized throughout the world for excellence.

Earlier the Southern Baptist Convention had rescued the two ailing "eight percenters" promoted by James Jennings.

In 1950 the city of Phoenix was a relatively small commercial center, surrounded by rich agricultural lands, midway between El Paso and Los Angeles. The population of Maricopa County that year was 331,770. Only 32 percent of this population lived within the city limits.

In 1960 there were 663,510 people living in Maricopa County and 66 percent of these lived within the city limits of Phoenix. While the hospitals struggled to meet the increased demand for health care, the community was busy answering other needs.

In the late 1930's, Mrs. Maie Bartlett Heard, widow of the long-time publisher of *The Arizona Republic,* and her son, Bartlett, had given the city a square block of ground located at the northeast corner of McDowell Road and Central Avenue. They proposed the land be used for a library, an art gallery, and the Phoenix Little Theatre, which was then occupying an old red brick coach house facing McDowell Road midway between Central and First Street. When the gift was received the city lacked the resources and the will to do anything about it. In the late '40s a civic center association was formed under the leadership of Frank Snell, Walter Bimson and local philanthropist Alfred Knight. Bimson and Snell undertook to raise funds for the construction of the art center.

In 1951 the city constructed a new central library at this site, the art center was built, and a new Phoenix Little Theater building constructed on the northeast corner of the plot.

In 1947 Dr. Howell Randolph, long-time chief of staff at St. Luke's Hospital and a pioneer thoracic surgeon, and four civic leaders: Mrs. Charles Korrick, Mrs. Fred Blair Townsend, Dr. Oscar Thoeny, and Gertrude Zorne, created the Phoenix Symphony Association.

Municipal bond issues financed the extension of the sewer system northward to the Arizona Canal. The city bought dozens of small private water companies. An arrangement was reached with the Salt River Project permitting the city to deliver the agricultural water no longer needed by occupants of city lots through a domestic piped system after purification. This arrangement gave the city an assured supply of municipal and industrial water.

Del E. Webb, who as a young carpenter had built the house on 12th Street which Lulu Clifton occupied until she died, opened a new planned community on the desert west of Phoenix, which he called Sun City.

The new residents struggled valiantly to maintain the old casual lifestyle which had made life so charming in the early days. But the availability of refrigerated air conditioning and the increased traffic generated by this new population, coupled with the rapidly developing industrial growth, gradually ended the old ways. In 1950 only 15,700 Arizonans were employed in manufacturing. By 1960 that figure had risen to 49,200 and most of these industrial jobs were located in the Phoenix area.

Government expanded. The Valley National Bank became the largest bank in the Rocky Mountain region. Property values doubled and redoubled. Air transport was promising to make the warm winter climate of the Southwest easily available to fugitives from the eastern snow and ice. The tourist industry, served by magnificent new resorts, became a major factor in the Valley's economic growth.

This new population helped to alter the political complexion of Arizona. In territorial days and under statehood from 1912 to 1950, Arizona was truly a one-party state. In those 38 years, only two Republicans had been elected governor: Thomas Campbell and John C. Phillips. Campbell was elected in 1916, but the Arizona Supreme Court overturned the ballot box and awarded the office to George Wiley Paul Hunt. Campbell ran again in 1918 and served two years as governor. Phillips was elected in 1928 and served two years. No Republican had been elected to the U. S. House of Representatives. Only one Republican had been elected to the U. S. Senate and he served only one term.

In 1950 the Republicans shattered the domination of the Democrats on state offices with the election of Republican Howard Pyle as governor. Two years later Republicans Barry Goldwater and John Rhodes were elected to the Congress of the United States. Once narrowly parochial with a limited economic base, Phoenix in the decade of the '50s became a cosmopolitan, urbane, cultured community, with a multi-faceted economy.

In 1961, that bright and rosy future so clearly predicted by the accomplishments of the '50s was not all that apparent to the board of trustees of Good Samaritan Hospital. The old buildings constructed in the '20s and the '30s demanded constant repair and remodeling. The hospital was operating at near capacity, with an occupancy rate of 91 percent, and more space was desperately needed.

The inadequacies Administrator Stephen Morris had to cope with were far more complex than just a lack of beds and deteriorating buildings. The new age of medical specialties brought questions which had to be answered. The medical staff was, at times, impatient with the administration. In the new Cardiac Care Unit surgeons were replacing heart valves and repairing interventricular septal defects. More surgical space was needed; more highly trained technicians were called for.

To answer the space problem, a ground floor addition was added to B Wing and construction was commenced on a new two-story F Wing. Dr. C. Selby Mills was Chief of Staff and some of the medical men agitated for representation on the hospital board.

The heavy patient load helped to increase hospital income, but all the nurses, orderlies, and technicians were demanding an increase in salaries. The new departments placed an additional burden on the hospital's resources. In 1963 a Cystic Fibrosis Clinic was opened, 23,000 patients were admitted, and the hospital provided 154,748 outpatient services. To work in the field of mental health, a full-time psychiatrist was employed. Medical education and the intern program was costing half a million dollars a year.

In 1964 a new Kidney Treatment Center was opened, along with a new Department of Inhalation Therapy and a Pulmonary

Function Laboratory. The work performed by commercial laundries did not meet the rigid hospital demands for sterility. As first suggested by the Hamilton survey report, Good Samaritan opened a laundry to serve its own needs and also to do the laundry for St. Luke's and John C. Lincoln hospitals. The program of land acquisition was continued and as privately owned lots in the immediate area became available, they were purchased.

The Good Samaritan campus, which had been started with the gift of that one square block, had been gradually increased to include an area of six square blocks between Tenth Street and 12th Street and from McDowell Road to Culver Street.

CHAPTER 13

Merger and Purchase

The dramatic alterations which took place in the greater Phoenix community commencing in 1950 were highly visible. Among them were new subdivisions, gigantic retail shopping centers, new high rise office buildings in the inner core, the development of cultural resources and, in 1958, the long deserved upgrading of the status of the four-year educational institution at Tempe from Arizona State College to Arizona State University.

This change was the result of a vote by the people on an initiative measure placed on the general election ballot in 1958. The leaders in that drive to gain university status were Judge Walter Craig, Kathryn Gammage, wife of the president of the state college, former Republican Governor Howard Pyle, and James Creasman, an ASU alumnus who later became director of the university's special events and programs. Supporters of the University of Arizona in Tucson had successfully resisted earlier efforts, despite the fact that when the Board of Regents created four separate colleges at the institution in 1954, the state college became a university in fact, though not in name. The Board of Regents, undoubtedly influenced by University of Arizona loyalists, had refused to act. The newspaper reports of the jubilant celebration in the Valley following the success of the initiative overlooked an amusing historical irony. When the 13th Territorial Legislature in 1885 was considering establishing a university, the Maricopa County legislators chose to let the school go to Tucson and have the territorial insane asylum located in Phoenix because they thought it would be a greater stimulus to the local economy.

The significant change in approach to answering the health care needs of the people of the Salt River Valley was more the result of chance than design. In the business world the sole proprietor had all but disappeared. The corner grocery gave way to giant food store chains, first pioneered in Arizona by George Mickle and D. J. Peters who organized the Pay'N-Takit stores in the '20s. The economies of scale conferred benefits on the consumer. By 1960 those individually-owned pioneer department stores had all been absorbed by regional or national organizations. The Goldwater stores were sold to Associated Dry Goods. Dayton Hudson absorbed Diamond's Boston Store. The Korrick family sold out to The Broadway. Americans bought automobiles manufactured by the "Big Four." The steel industry was dominated by three or four conglomerates. Gasoline was marketed through chain retail outlets owned by the major petroleum producers. Banks and insurance companies merged.

Since David confronted Goliath the myth that "big is bad" has been perpetuated, and in the ongoing struggle for economic and social equality, populist demagogues have inveighed against the concentration of wealth and power. Historians of this new trend in economic development generally agree the motivation for this change was more than the inability of the independent to successfully compete against the giant. The inheritance tax laws greatly influenced the decisions of the owner-operator to sell out, in anticipation of that certain day when a death in the family would demand a liquidity to pay the taxes. In the field of agriculture, the small farmer with limited capital has been gradually absorbed into a corporate operation large enough to survive a poor crop year in a capital-intensive industry.

The Phoenix area hospitals were confronted with increasing capital demands, not only to buy the bricks and mortar necessary to meet the community needs, but also to finance the emerging special services resulting from the new understandings and technologies. In the 1960's, in addition to its specialized Coronary Care Unit, Good Samaritan opened an Institute of Rehabilitation Medicine, a Kidney Center, and a Department of Inhalation Therapy and Pulmonary Function. A new five-story building was completed to house the long-term care and rehab facility. The Kidney Center sponsored home dialysis. A new Institute of Gastroenterology, with internationally-known Dr. David Sun as director, was launched. In an effort to reduce the infant death rate, a neonatalogist was hired and a Newborn Intensive Care Unit created. The other major community hospitals in the area joined this effort. The incidence of infant death in Arizona had ranked the state 40th in the nation. This has been improved to place Arizona in the fifth position.

The need for community-wide planning, cooperation among the hospitals, and restricting proliferation of special services was emphasized in the Hamilton and Community Council reports.

In an article published in 1967 in Good Samaritan's quarterly house organ, *Care*, Administrator Stephen Morris examined the challenge facing hospitals. Philanthropic support was no longer capable of meeting capital needs, fragmentation of facilities had created unnecessary costs, there was needless duplication of services, and the revenues generated were not sufficient to provide the high quality expert management available in other areas of the private sector. Financial planning, the development of new resources, expansion of facilities, and recruitment of personnel, all required specialized talents the hospitals could not afford to purchase. There was no specific call for merger or consolidation, but that possibility emerged as an inescapable conclusion of his review of the realities.

Scott Parker, a hospital administrator in Minneapolis, read the Morris article. It was still fresh in his mind when the board of trustees of the troubled Southside Hospital in Mesa persuaded him to come to Arizona and take command of what was then the only hospital facility in the East Valley.

Mesa and the neighboring small community of Lehi were both colonized by Mormon immigrants from Utah. The descendants of those brave pioneers, who had made the long wagon trip from Missouri to Salt Lake to escape religious persecution, brought their courage and zeal, their strict moral codes and their community of love and compassion to Central Arizona in 1878. Jacob Hamblin led the way. On their southward trip they triumphed over that great natural barrier, the Grand Canyon of the Colorado, by partially disassembling their wagons and lowering them over the precipitous cliffs by ropes to ford the river and continue south. Some of them stopped in the mountain meadow lands above the Mogollon Rim, establishing the settlements of Eagar, Snowflake, Show Low, Springerville, St. Johns, Woodruff and Shumway. The City of Mesa was incorporated in July of 1883 under the leadership of T. C. Sirrine, C. I. Robson, G. W. Sirrine, and F. M.

Pomeroy. They planted their cypress trees and made the streets 130 feet wide.

The not-for-profit Southside Hospital was incorporated by Elijah Allen, Ida Arnold, C. H. Russell, C. A. Roberts, Lottie Holcomb and C. M. Gerrard in 1923. They bought a residence at the corner of East Main and Hibbert, owned by Mr. and Mrs. J. T. Lesueur. The two-story building was converted into a seven-bed hospital. A financial report submitted to the board of trustees, covering the month of August, 1923, shows cash receipts of $954.94. Among the bills paid that month was one for hay provided by the Pew brothers for $36.40. The hay was for the hospital's milk cow.

In the early '30s the Lesueur residence was torn down to make way for a new wing with 37 beds. Doctor B. B. Moeur of Tempe, who was on the staff of Southside and was elected Governor of Arizona in 1932, helped the hospital secure some funding from the WPA project. The City of Mesa and private contributors provided the rest. There were eight doctors on the hospital staff, including five from Tempe and one from Chandler. During the years of World War II, when Williams Field was established, additional separate buildings were constructed.

In 1967 Southside Hospital was in deep trouble. Four of its five wings had been rated structurally deficient by the State Health Department. The spread-out complex was inefficient, the mechanical equipment inadequate.

A 1965 report by James A. Hamilton Associates said, "The inefficiencies of the spread-out complex of units, such as are present at Southside District Hospital, are very significant. Supplies must move great horizontal distances to reach often-used departments of the hospital. Mechanical equipment, such as pneumatic tube systems, dumbwaiters, package conveyors, and the like, are normally used to cut down on the amount of personnel traveling in a hospital. This is impossible with the type of spread-out hospital as has been developed."

A new 170-bed Lutheran hospital had been opened at 525 West Brown Road in Mesa and admissions at Southside had fallen drastically.

Hamilton Associates recommended construction of a new Mesa-Tempe community hospital of at least 225 beds to be located midway between the two cities. The trustees purchased 58 acres of land at Southern Avenue and Dobson Road and members of the pioneer Dobson family contributed 26 acres adjacent to the new site.

When Scott Parker arrived in Mesa in 1967, the board of trustees attempted to form a Mesa-Tempe hospital district with authority to issue bonds and raise the estimated $6 million needed to build a new facility. The proposal was defeated at the polls. In Minneapolis Parker had witnessed the development of the Fairview Hospital Organization, a system of satellite hospitals combining suburban and metropolitan facilities.

In the fall of 1967, with the full approval of the trustees of Southside, Parker approached Good Samaritan with a request that the city hospital consider a merger with Southside and construct the projected new facilities at 1400 South Dobson Road.

The obvious beneficiaries of the proposed merger would be the residents of the Valley. A new and modern hospital located in the center of this growing residential area would improve the quality of health care available. More doctors would be attracted to the neighborhood. There would be a tremendous saving in travel time for patients and patient relatives.

The Health Facilities Planning Council and its executive director, Milton Gan, endorsed the proposal. Both hospital boards would lose some of their autonomy in the merger. Southside would lose its identity. Samaritan would have to call on all its resources to provide the estimated $15 million required for construction.

In February of 1968 the boards of trustees of both hospitals announced their intention to carry out the merger. It took eight months to work out the details. The formal agreement was signed the second day of August, 1968. The new institution would be named Desert Samaritan. Five of the 13 members of the Southside Hospital board and the hospital's chief of staff would become members of the Good Samaritan board of trustees. The remaining Southside board members and selected community leaders from Mesa and Tempe would become members of an advisory board for the operation of Desert Samaritan.

Morris says, "It was an opportunity for us to expand our base and increase our service to the public. We knew there would be substantial savings in the cost of health care as a result of central management. Good Samaritan's occupancy rate was running about 90 percent. We thought it made much better sense to locate the new building where the people lived than it would be to increase the number of beds on the Samaritan campus. We recognized the risk involved, but the potential benefits were so obvious we really had no other choice. We did not intend to duplicate any of the extremely expensive specialities we were operating at Good Samaritan. Patients requiring this kind of care would be transferred to one of the central hospitals. The vast majority of those admitted to the new Desert Samaritan would be able to receive all the care they needed in that location."

Planning and construction took four years. The design of the building, with patient rooms in pods around a central nursing station, was considered revolutionary. It eliminated the long horizontal travel identified as one of the glaring deficiencies at the old Southside institution. This new configuration provides the nurses with a much better opportunity for constant supervision of the patient and, at the same time, reduces demand on the personnel. The benefits of the merger were apparent even before the new building was constructed. Admissions in 1970 were 26 percent above those in 1965. Utilization is one of the key factors in the containment of health care costs.

On the west side of the Valley the hospital at Maryvale, constructed with funds from first mortgage revenue bonds bearing eight percent interest, had been plagued with financial problems from the day it opened. Four million, four hundred thousand dollars worth of these bonds had been sold to individuals and organizations throughout the United States.

To meet construction cost overruns, an additional $400,000 in bonds had to be sold. Patient revenues were inadequate to operate the hospital and pay the interest on this indebtedness. Some of the bond holders filed a suit against the promoters and management in federal court, requesting the appointment of a receiver and alleging violations of the security laws and civil fraud.

At the request of the original indenture trustee, Lane Title and Trust Company, which filed a foreclosure action, the matter was transferred from federal court to state court, an action agreed to by the original litigant, John L. Roberts. The state court appointed Duke Gaskin, M.D., and Fred Foster, administrator of the Maricopa County Hospital, as co-receivers.

In 1964 the federal court assumed control and appointed a new administrator, Roland Wilpitz, from the Marcus Lawrence Hospital in Cottonwood. Wilpitz resigned, the court appointed Frank Dunning as trustee and Dunning hired Rod Cleland, who had been in management at the Arizona State Hospital for the Insane, to be the administrator. Cleland was more successful than his predecessors. Revenues gradually increased, a stronger medical staff was recruited, and in 1964 the hospital resumed making interest payments on the indebtedness.

In 1967 Cleland resigned, to be replaced by James Thomas. In 1968 American Medical Enterprises, Inc., a Los Angeles corporation which operates a chain of for-profit hospitals, made a bid to the federal court to purchase Maryvale Community Hospital.

The Maricopa County Health Facilities Planning Council expressed its opposition to the sale of Maryvale to an out-of-state for-profit corporation. The council, with the full cooperation of the existing not-for-profit hospitals in the community, was struggling to contain health care costs. The record of for-profit institutions in other parts of the country was, they said, not consistent with that objective. The for-profits provided excellent facilities and were well managed, but they were organized to make money. Community service was secondary.

The council approached John C. Lincoln and St. Joseph's, requesting that one or both of these local not-for-profit hospitals acquire Maryvale. The trustees of John C. Lincoln concluded they lacked the necessary financial base. St. Joseph's gave the matter serious consideration and until a few weeks before the sale was to take place under court order, it was believed that St. Joseph's would enter a bid.

At almost the last minute, those in authority at St. Joseph's concluded it was not in their best interest to buy Maryvale. Milton Gan, then executive secretary of the Health Planning Council, approached the trustees of Good Samaritan.

Morris says, "It was a very difficult decision for our board to make. We had just completed the merger with Southside. We had the financial capacity; that is, we could borrow the necessary funds. We would have preferred the hospital go to either Lincoln or St. Joseph's, but we were up against a deadline. There was great community pressure to keep Maryvale a locally owned, locally operated hospital.

"Judge Carl Muecke of the federal court, who was conducting the sale, was sitting in San Diego that summer of 1968. Our board of trustees agonized over the decision, but they finally sent me to California with authority to bid $5,110,000 for Maryvale."

The purchase was formally completed on September 23, 1968. All the bond holders were repaid in full, including back interest; all the hospital debts were paid, and there was $800,000 in cash and accounts receivable left over. *The Arizona Republic* said editorially, "We are glad Good Samaritan will get the Maryvale property. Local administration should best out-of-state ownership."

The Samaritan Health Service system of hospitals was established in response to community need. Southside approached Samaritan because it lacked the financial base to provide adequate service. Maryvale was purchased because both the citizen committee and the medical community believe the public would be better served by local ownership and management. Morris says, "The idea for merger and acquisition did not originate within the Good Samaritan organization, but the concept is sound. Since that beginning we have clearly demonstrated that a system of hospitals, operating under the supervision of central management, can provide the community with better medical care at a lower cost."

Northwest Hospital, a not-for-profit "eight percenter" institution, had severe difficulties from the day it opened its doors in Glendale in 1960. There was a lack of solid community support, the facility was too small to attract the strong medical staff essential to success, the cashflow was submarginal, there were no funds for enlargement or improvement. It had been financed through the sale of $700,000 worth of eight percent bonds.

In 1966 the hospital paid off the bond holders in full, after negotiating a new 15-year mortgage loan of $550,000 at 6.8 percent interest from the Valley National Bank. But this reduction in carrying costs on the indebtedness was not sufficient to make the hospital truly solvent. In 1969 Thomas O. Geist, Administrator of Northwest, approached both Good Samaritan Hospitals, Inc. (the new corporate name for Good Samaritan's system) and John C. Lincoln with a request for merger. Geist said many of the accounts were six months delinquent, there was no money for renovation or maintenance, much of the equipment was obsolescent, and he was unable to respond to requests from the medical staff to provide 24-hour emergency service. There was no employee retirement program or major medical hospital insurance coverage.

On August 13, 1969, Northwest was merged with Samaritan Hospitals. Five members of Northwest's board of trustees were designated to serve on Samaritan's board of trustees, along with the hospital's chief of staff. Samaritan made a non-interest interhospital loan in the amount of $100,000. These funds were used to retire Northwest's outstanding operating indebtedness. Plans were made and a general contractor employed to modernize the Northwest radiology department. A new and larger emergency room was constructed, a three-bed recovery room was built adjacent to the surgeries, an employees benefit program in existence at Samaritan was extended to the employees at Northwest, and a new hospital dietitian was provided. But the size of the physical plant and the lack of strong community support were still problems. The facility was renamed Glendale Samaritan Hospital.

These mergers made it possible to combine the resources, financial and human, of the community hospital. Their identity was preserved and their community support continued. Still local in nature, they enjoyed the benefits of the system. The boards of trustees and the management of these smaller institutions chose to become a part of the system because they recognized it was the only way to improve the quality and quantity of local health care, and adequately address the problem of increasing hospital costs.

Facing competition from the giant chains of hospitals operated for profit, individual community hospitals throughout the nation are now following the pattern first established in Phoenix by the board of trustees of Samaritan which responded affirmatively to the requests for assistance from Southside, Maryvale and Northwest.

CHAPTER 14

System Benefits Extended to Rural Areas

In 1969 Good Samaritan Hospitals signed lease agreements to manage Navapache Hospital in Lakeside, the Holbrook hospital, Grand Canyon Hospital on the south rim, and the White Mountain Community Hospital in Springerville.

Navapache Hospital was formed as a result of a merger of the Josephine Goldwater Hospital in Show Low and the James G. McNary Hospital in McNary. A. L. Armstrong, M.D., and a group of citizens organized the Show Low Community Hospital Committee and "hospital guild" in the 1950's. Following a number of community fund drives and generous contributions from Josephine Williams Goldwater, a pioneer Arizona nurse, her two sons, U. S. Senator Barry and Phoenix businessman Bob, and her daughter, Carolyn, Josephine Goldwater Hospital was opened in Show Low in 1961.

Thirty miles to the southeast, in the lumber town of McNary, the Southwest Lumber Mills had for 50 years been providing medical care for the lumber company's employees and for residents of the McNary/Pinetop/Lakeside area. By 1965 this company-owned subsidized facility had become a 15-bed hospital providing emergency and outpatient care. Southwest Lumber Mills had changed hands. The new name was Southwest Forest Industries and the new president was J. B. Edens.

Until the 1950's these little settlements in the high White Mountain country had enjoyed very little growth. Show Low, Lakeside, Springerville, Taylor, and Woodruff were all Mormon communities. They were supply centers for the farmers and ranchers.

The lumber mill at McNary had been developed by southern interests, and most of their labor force was black. In the late '50s and early '60s the entire area became extremely popular as a summer vacation retreat. Near Pinetop a group of Phoenicians acquired some land and built an exciting golf course, surrounded by three or four hundred summer cabins.

Milt Coggins, son of L. W. Coggins, who had served so long on the board of trustees of Good Samaritan Hospital, designed the golf course. The summer homes were quite elaborate. Between Memorial Day and Labor Day the rich and the powerful from the Valley gathered on the veranda of the White Mountain Country Club.

A second golf course was built just across the highway and called Pinetop. Developed under the sponsorship of Gray Madison, a successful automobile dealer and one of the state's leading amateur golfers, Pinetop was an instant success. The development of these recreational facilities, plus the fishing and hiking resources of the area, caused an economic boom. The price of land suitable for development doubled and tripled, and in the summer time neither the 15-bed McNary Hospital or the tiny Josephine Goldwater institution were able to meet the growing communities' medical needs. In 1965 the Construction and Planning Division of the Arizona State Department of Health, the state agency responsible for the distribution of Hill-Burton (Hill-Harris) federal money, declared both the McNary and the Josephine Goldwater hospitals out of conformance with federal requirements.

The McNary hospital applied for $375,000 in Hill-Burton funds to construct a new institution on a site leased from the White Mountain Apache Indian Tribe. The request was approved. At the same time, the Josephine Goldwater Hospital board requested funds to remodel its facilities. The state agency suggested the hospitals merge.

The Goldwater-McNary Navapache Hospital District was formed, embracing the area of the high school districts of McNary, Alchesay on the Apache Indian Reservation, Blue Ridge, Show Low, and Snowflake. Six hundred twenty-one thousand dollars of Hill-Burton funds was made available. The district sold bonds amounting to $750,000. The Phelps Dodge Corporation offered to contribute a 20-acre site two and one-half miles south of Show Low and three miles north of Lakeside. This offer was accepted and the combined hospital boards commenced to plan for construction.

Most of the real leaders in this effort to meet the medical needs of the area were from the Phoenix area. As one local resident put it, "We passed our bond issue, then realized we really didn't know anything about building a modern hospital." The hospital trustees, with the full support of the White Mountain medical community, approached Good Samaritan with a request for help. As a result, a seven-year management lease agreement, with a five-year renewal option, was signed and the new facility was constructed.

Holbrook, the county seat of Navajo County, once headquarters for the vast operations of the Hashknife Land and Cattle Company, was originally named Horsehead Crossing. When the Atlantic and Pacific Railroad was constructed across Arizona the name was changed to Holbrook, in honor of the line's chief engineer. Originally it was a part of Yavapai County and was the scene of one of the West's most famous gunfights between Sheriff Commodore Owens, the Coopers, and the Blevins. Its most popular saloon was the Bucket of Blood. It is the gateway to the nearby Petrified Forest National Park and the vast Navajo Indian Reservation.

In 1964 the city sold $450,000 of hospital bonds, was granted $125,000 in Hill-Burton funds, and a new 25-bed hospital was opened. The facilities included a pathological laboratory, X-ray equipment, a nursery with a special isolation section, a delivery room with two-bed labor rooms adjoining, laboratory, and an emergency room that could handle six patients. This latter facility was particularly important, because 25 percent of those coming to the hospital were trauma patients, victims of vehicle accidents on Highway 66.

From the day it opened, the Holbrook hospital had trouble recruiting and maintaining doctors, the management was inadequate, and it was under-utilized. In 1969 a management agreement was signed with Good Samaritan Hospitals.

When Grand Canyon National Park was created in February, 1919, the U. S. Department of the Interior assumed responsibility of providing medical care for the hundreds of thousands of visitors who came each year to view America's greatest tourist attraction. In 1929 the government built a 10-bed hospital adjacent to the hotel and camp ground operated by Fred Hervey. The building was a rambling log cabin. The intention was to lease the facility to a doctor, who would establish permanent residence and take care of the visitors, the year-round employees of a hotel and camp ground, and the rangers who supervised the park. The population was seasonal. In the summer, when the special Santa Fe trains brought thousands of visitors from the main line at Williams, there was more than one doctor could do. In winter there were not enough permanent residents to keep even one doctor busy, let alone support the necessary nurses and technicians. Doctors came and went.

In 1964 the Park Service signed a five-year contract with Dr. Rafael Garbayo to operate the hospital. When Garbayo came to Grand Canyon the community had been without any doctor for four months. Residents were required to travel 60 miles to Williams or 78 miles to Flagstaff for medical care.

In 1968 the Park Service built a new 22-bed facility at a cost of $800,000. It was well designed and well equipped, including space for a dentist and a medical office suite. When his contract was up, Dr. Garbayo left. He said that in summer the workload was much too heavy and, despite all of his efforts to recruit physicians from other areas, it just had not worked out. In September of 1969 the Park Service signed a seven-year concession agreement, with a seven-year renewal option, with Good Samaritan Hospitals.

In Round Valley, ten miles west of the New Mexico border, the Mormon settlements of Springerville and Eagar had suffered with inadequate medical care from the time the settlements were established. Babies were delivered by midwives trained in Salt Lake City, and only now and then was there a qualified physician available. In the early 1930s, a ten-bed hospital was constructed but there were not enough patients to attract any doctors on a permanent basis. The hospital was operated on an off again/on again erratic schedule.

In 1958 it closed once more. In 1959 the White Mountain Community Hospital, Inc. was formed by a group of concerned citizens. According to *The Phoenix Gazette*, nearly every family in the area pledged continuing financial support. A new doctor was recruited, a clinic was built, and it was proposed to add a new 25-bed wing, estimated to cost $150,000. It was to include a new surgical suite, recovery rooms, nursery, and a doctors' lounge.

The new wing was never started, but the community did not give up. In 1966, with $300,000 in Hill-Harris funds and a considerable sum raised locally, a new building was constructed. The following year, Stanley Shumway of St. Johns, a native of the White Mountains and a successful businessman, was named administrator. The board of trustees renewed their effort to solve the hospital's financial problems. In July of 1968 actor John Wayne, who owned a ranch in Springerville, supported a fund raising effort which produced $5,500.

In May of 1969 the board of trustees of White Mountain approached Samaritan Hospitals in Phoenix, asking to be rescued. In October a seven-year management lease was signed with Good Samaritan Hospitals.

Morris says, "We went into these lease management agreements with our eyes open. We knew the problems. We knew that at least for the foreseeable future they could not be made self-supporting, but these communities needed medical service. And with our resources we thought we could recruit the necessary personnel, reduce overhead, and ultimately achieve at least a break even point in the operations."

The principal cause of Arizona's disgracefully high infant mortality rate was isolation, vast populations on the Indian reservations in the northern part of the state, and inadequate facilities in the rural communities. Surface transport was too slow to meet the needs of the critically ill and the newborns, whose survival depended upon treatment in one of the great general hospitals in the Phoenix area. St. Luke's, St. Joseph's, John C. Lincoln, and Good Samaritan all had the specialized facilities and medical staffs necessary.

In 1969, with the help of the Kellogg Foundation, Good Samaritan organized AirEvac, a fixed-wing transportation service, to provide swift transport from the remote areas. All the hospitals in the Samaritan system, including those operated on management contracts, benefited from being able to communicate and consult with the specialists at Good Samaritan by telephone. The establishment of AirEvac made these resources available to rural patients whose condition required transfer. These fully equipped, competently staffed air ambulances were available to transport critical patients from anywhere in the state to any hospital in the metropolitan Phoenix area. AirEvac was quickly recognized as a major contributor to the reduction of infant death.

The rates charged were roughly comparable to ground transport. Its operation requires a substantial subsidy from the parent hospital system, but it is a proven life-saving instrument. In 1979 the service was expanded by the addition of a helicopter, as a joint venture between Samaritan and John C. Lincoln. The use of these machines, which can land directly on the roof of the hospitals or on an adjacent pad, is now commonplace. Although John C. Lincoln withdrew from the cooperative venture because of the costs in 1981, the Samaritan system continues to operate two helicopters, an Alouette 3, two fixed-wing aircraft, and an A-Star long-range helicopter. Phoenix Baptist Hospitals operate their own airborne transport. In 1982, 1,827 patients were taken to area hospitals in AirEvac helicopters. Approximately 70 percent were taken to hospitals other than those in the Samaritan system.

CHAPTER 15

New Demands—
New Answers

In the mid-1970s, that torrid romance between the Valley communities and growth commenced to cool. The surface streets were choked with traffic. On the only freeway, the cars and trucks were bumper to bumper all day long. That clean air, once the distinguishing characteristic of the Southwest, was discolored with pollutants from industry and the automobiles. The residential population had followed the stores and shops to the suburbs. Lawyers and bankers, police and judges, came to work each morning in downtown Phoenix, most of them went home at five, and few lived in the central city. The vagrant and the homeless took over the sidewalks and parks after dark.

Jobs in high tech manufacturing increased in number and importance. Motorola brought thousands of hourly employees to its new plant on the southern limits of Scottsdale and to a second installation on McDowell Road in Phoenix. Then a new third plant was constructed in the Mesa-Tempe area.

General Electric sold its plant in Deer Valley to Honeywell. Sperry Flight Systems expanded at the Deer Valley Airport, and Garrett increased its work force at Sky Harbor Airport.

Employment in manufacturing in Arizona increased from 15,700 in 1950 to 152,400 in 1980. Most of these new jobs were in the greater Phoenix area.

All this new population had to be transported from home to work. The automobile was the favorite mode. A difference of opinion over the proper location of an east-west freeway stopped construction after most of the right-of-way had been purchased, leaving a desolate belt of vacant property, with here and there a rundown building, stretching east to west from 21st Street to 15th Avenue, across the heart of what had once been a desirable residential neighborhood.

There were new demands on the city's limited supply of domestic and industrial water. The Central Arizona Project, designed to bring in supplemental water from the Colorado River, became a first priority. Some of the industries upon which the city had become so dependent demanded reductions in their rates for power, water and sewage service.

The Charter Government organization, which had been responsible for so many years of effective representative citizen rule at City Hall, grew old and tired. In 1976 a non-charter candidate was elected mayor. The city, recognizing the change taking place in downtown, and hoping to stem the tide, built a gigantic civic center. The old Adams Hotel was torn down and a new one erected in its place. Where Dorris-Heyman had sold furniture and Goldwater's offered "The Best Always," the ground was taken over for a parking garage. A new downtown commercial hotel, the Hyatt Regency, was constructed between Adams and Monroe, First and Second Streets, adjacent to the new Civic Center. The main Post Office was moved to a more convenient location on Buckeye Road. The once proud Westward Ho Hotel, facing bankruptcy, was converted into a senior citizens' residence.

In an effort to cope with all of these growth-related problems, community leaders called for long-range planning. Hundreds of private citizens were enlisted, and task forces were formed to study and question the community's social, economic, and educational structures. Special attention was focused on the health care providers. When the Valley's hospitals refused to grant preferred volume discounts to Motorola, the company orchestrated and financed a campaign attacking the merits and motives of the administrators of the Valley hospitals, with Samaritan Health Service being the primary target of this assault.

In 1970 Good Samaritan Hospitals amended its corporate structure and changed the name to Samaritan Health Service. The move was necessary in order to improve the management structure now responsible for the operation of four hospitals in metropolitan Phoenix and meet its contract responsibilities to the four rural hospitals. Morris was named president and CEO of the new corporation, and a central office was established on North Third

Street. Representative community-minded individuals, volunteers serving without pay on an enlarged board of directors, continued to determine overall policy.

One of the most obvious benefits of the new structure was its increased financial strength, an ability to provide the capital funding necessary to keep up with the increased demand.

The board of directors of that proprietary hospital started by Dr. Ginn approached Samaritan with an offer to sell the facility on East Thomas Road. After months of negotiation, the Samaritan board declined the offer.

In 1970 a group of local investors bought the hospital and operated it as a "for-profit" until 1978, when the institution was taken over by the giant for-profit hospital chain, Humana. It has been enlarged and remodeled.

In 1971 a merger was accomplished with the Tri-City Mental Health Center, an organization formed by citizens of the Mesa-Tempe-Chandler area. SHS was to provide management and medical support — policies to be determined by a community advisory board — and the five offices, offering counseling in psychiatric and mental health matters, were placed under the supervision of the administration of Desert Samaritan Hospital.

The new Desert Samaritan facility was completed and opened in 1972. The SHS board of directors donated the old facilities in Mesa to that community for use by the city's non-profit community agencies.

Both the Hamilton survey and the Community Council survey had identified the establishment of a cooperative laundry service as one area where hospitals could save money and provide better service. In 1972 SHS completed a $3.5 million facility to provide for the laundry needs of the four hospitals in the SHS system. In 1974 a separate entity, the Arizona Hospital Service Corporation, was created to operate the laundry and to permit other hospitals in the Phoenix area to enjoy the benefits of this specialized facility. AHSC commenced providing services to Samaritan Health Service, John C. Lincoln, St. Luke's, Boswell Memorial, Phoenix General, and three hospitals in Tucson: St. Mary's, St. Joseph's, and Tucson General.

AHSC is operated by a board of directors consisting of two representatives from each member hospital, with the physical plant leased from SHS. In addition to the 11 not-for-profit hospitals in Phoenix and Tucson, the laundry serves Arizona Children's

Hospital, Arizona Training Center, Luke Air Force Base, Chandler Community Hospital, and Phoenix Memorial Hospital. There were no commercial laundry facilities available which were capable of meeting the aseptic standards required for hospital usage. The participating institutions were able to lower their laundry costs. In 1982 the facility handled 18,000,000 pounds of soiled linens, providing for the needs of approximately 4,300 patient beds per day.

In 1973 the Samaritan Health Service management contract with the Holbrook Hospital was terminated. In August of that year the Samaritan School of Nursing was closed. The financial burden of operating a resident boarding school, plus increased emphasis on the importance of baccalaureate training for nurses, dictated the closing.

The demands imposed on the nation's health care provider system by Medicaid and Medicare created new problems for the hospitals. Originally sponsored by church-related organizations and funded by charitable contributions, the hospitals were no longer able to satisfy their capital needs from this source. With the government assuming increasing responsibility for health, education, and welfare, private giving diminished.

A new mechanism was desperately needed to meet capital needs. Legislation was passed authorizing local governments to cooperate in the issuance of so-called "industrial bonds," exempt from both state and federal taxation. Amortization and interest must be paid by the recipient institutions.

Funding from this source has been used to provide housing at lower than market cost, build industrial plants to increase employment, and are the best and cheapest source of money to meet the capital needs of the not-for-profit hospitals. The obligations are not backed by the full faith and credit of the authorizing governmental entity and represent no liability for the taxpayers.

In 1975, by an amendment to the SHS articles of incorporation, all ties with the Methodist Church were permanently dissolved. This action permitted SHS to qualify for financing through the tax exempt bond mechanism.

Morris, who admits the formation of the SHS hospital system was brought about more by an effort to solve local problems than by design, believes the system organization offers the best solution to the nation's health care problems.

HAROLD L. DIVELBESS
Long-time chairman of the board of trustees, Good Samaritan Hospital. Members of his law firm, John L. Gust and Frank O. Smith, preceded him in service on the hospital board.

RONALD WARNER

WILLIAM P. REILLY
Civic and business leader who has contributed greatly of his talents in support of St. Joseph's Hospital.

EARL BIMSON
Son of Walter R. Bimson and long-time member of the Good Samaritan board of trustees.

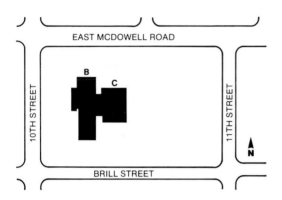

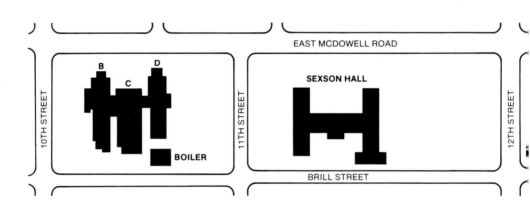

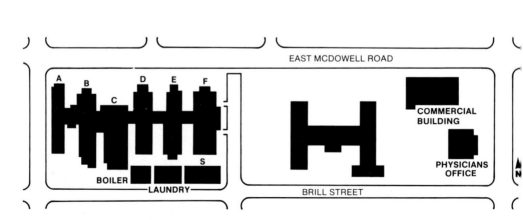

SCHEMATICS OF GROWTH OF GOOD SAMARITAN HOSPITAL
(Plats 1918-1930, 1930-1954, 1954-1966)
The hospital Miss Lulu started grew and grew and grew.

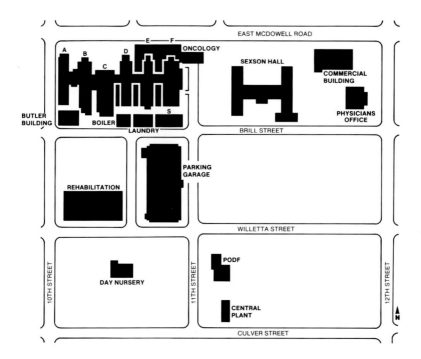

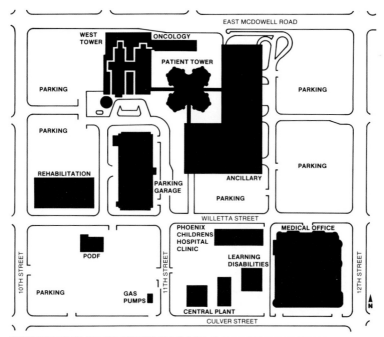

SCHEMATICS OF GROWTH OF GOOD SAMARITAN HOSPITAL
(Plats 1966-1977 and 1977-1984)
. . . and grew and grew.

ST. JOSEPH'S HOSPITAL
North 4th Street, about 1913.

MODERN ST. JOSEPH'S HOSPITAL

MODERN JOHN C. LINCOLN HOSPITAL

MODERN ST. LUKE'S HOSPITAL AND MEDICAL CENTER

DESERT SAMARITAN HOSPITAL

MARYVALE SAMARITAN HOSPITAL

NEW GOOD SAMARITAN MEDICAL CENTER

THUNDERBIRD SAMARITAN HOSPITAL

DAVE REED
President, Samaritan Health Service; Chief Executive Officer, Samaritan Health Service and SamCor.

HARRY J. CAVANAGH
Chairman of the Board, Samaritan Health Service

JAMES P. SIMMONS
Chairman of the Board, SamCor

"Even before we were approached by Southside," Morris says, "I was becoming conscious of the fact that at Good Sam we were over-specialized. Too many of our beds were devoted to the extraordinary requirements of patients needing these special medical services. As a single institution, we were over-managed. We had built up a staff of industrial relations people — industrial engineers, cost analysts, certified public accountants, and legal advisors. All of these special skills were needed but under-utilized.

"After the merger with Southside and the acquisition of Maryvale and Northwest, we were able to spread this expertise throughout the entire system without enlarging the staffs. We could establish levels of care in the satellite institutions, and thus spread the increase in costs at Good Samaritan, which is the flagship of the system."

Stephen Morris recognized the possibility that Phoenix could become a regional medical center. There was no logical reason for the people in the Rocky Mountain states to travel to Houston, to the Mayo Clinic, to Johns Hopkins, to Massachusetts General, or to Scripps in La Jolla, when Phoenix had the facilities and the medical talent much closer to their homes.

What Morris envisioned was a contained environment where all of the amenities could be available — a hotel for patient relatives and ambulatory patients, shops, medical offices, recreational facilities — all in a park-like setting with open spaces and landscaping. Located almost midway between St. Joseph's and St. Luke's, the facilities could accommodate out-of-city patients being treated at these institutions.

The Good Samaritan medical campus, approximately 33 acres, was located in the center of a blighted downtown residential area ripe for redevelopment. A new east-west crosstown freeway, bordering hospital property on the south, was in an advanced stage of planning. The first step was to do something about the ancient physical facilities at Good Samaritan. The plant had been remodeled and enlarged horizontally to a point where it suffered from the same inherent inefficiencies which had prompted the abandonment of the Southside Hospital plant in Mesa.

The central tower concept, introduced in this area with the construction of Desert Samaritan, had more than demonstrated its superior capabilities.

In 1978 ground was broken for a new 770-bed hospital. The design called for a 12-story patient tower, connected to a four-story nucleus for all emergency, operating, and ancillary services. Some of the newer portions of the old hospital facilities were retained and renovated for administrative use and non-patient functions.

In 1977 Samaritan Health Service, in cooperation with Mesa General, Tempe Community and Desert Samaritan, established the East Valley Health Service Center to handle medical emergencies in the Apache Junction area.

In 1978 the board of directors of Samaritan Health Service authorized the founding of a non-profit corporation to consolidate and coordinate fund raising efforts and to receive philanthropic gifts.

In October, 1978, John C. Lincoln and Samaritan Health Service entered into a cooperative joint venture agreement to construct a proposed Lincoln-Samaritan Hospital and Health Center in the northwest Valley, as a replacement for the inadequate, outmoded Glendale Samaritan. To accomplish this, SHS established a new hospital corporation. John C. Lincoln did the same. This arrangement permitted both parent organizations to retain their separate identities while cooperating to meet an established community need. Initially Phoenix Baptist was invited to become a part of this joint venture effort. When Phoenix Baptist declined participation, John C. Lincoln and Samaritan assumed the total responsibility.

In 1979, while the facilities were still in the planning stage, Lincoln-Samaritan entered into a joint venture with Camelback to construct and operate a 75-bed psychiatric unit on the campus of the new Lincoln-Samaritan Hospital and Health Center. Ground was broken for the new facility in January of 1982 and it is expected construction will be completed early in 1984.

Camelback Hospital, organized by Dr. Otto L. Bendheim, one of the Valley's earliest psychiatrists, was the first free-standing institution dedicated to meeting the Valley's mental health needs. Located in a country setting on North 34th Street, the facility provided 48 beds for both long-term and short-term patients.

The first Hamilton study recommended against such specialized hospitals and said, "A psychiatric service, properly organized and operated as a part of a general hospital program, can do much to help remove the stigma which, unfortunately, is still often associated with mental illnesses."

In order to carry out the cooperative venture it was necessary to secure the approval of the Central Arizona Health Systems Agency and the Department of Health Services. An application for a Certificate of Need was filed February 1, 1979. It was not approved until May 15, 1980. As a result of this 15-month delay, market forces driven by the highest inflationary rate in the nation's history substantially increased the ultimate cost.

In 1980 the residents of Pleasant Valley, under the Mogollon Rim in central Arizona, had only one doctor and were in danger of losing his services. The area around the little city of Young is celebrated in history and fiction as the location of the Pleasant Valley Wars between the feuding sheepmen and cattlemen. The community owned an old service station building which had been converted into a small medical center located on one acre of land.

William Peck, M.D., of Fort Lauderdale, Florida had tired of city life and decided to move to a smaller community. After trying Jackson Hole, Wyoming, Tucson, and Apache Junction, he moved to Young and accepted appointment as director of the Pleasant Valley Community Medical Center. But there were not enough patients to generate the very modest income Dr. Peck needed, so he had told the board he would have to move to a larger community.

Community leaders in this remote area approached Samaritan with a request for help. The hospital responded by putting Dr. Peck on its payroll and making him a member of the SHS medical staff. The Young facility is open two and one-half days a week and Dr. Peck responds to patients from his home when the center is closed.

Stephen Morris says, "Sure, we are subsidizing health care for the people in this isolated region, but at Good Samaritan we provide more than eight million dollars worth of medical care to charity patients each year. We just extended our outreach. Without our help, the ranchers, school teachers, and store keepers in the Pleasant Valley would have no medical care at all."

In 1980 Samaritan organized Health Enterprises, Inc., the first for-profit subsidiary designed to locate and operate alternative sources of revenue. Health Enterprises, Inc., which later was dissolved into DynaCor, a for-profit subsidiary of Samaritan Health Services' recently created holding company SamCor. This organization operates the laundry, provides consulting services to other organizations, and owns Standard Surgical Supply, which provides medical products to physicians and hospitals.

The board of directors of SHS viewed this new corporation as an opportunity to reduce health care costs and increase services to the community.

In 1980 the West Valley Emergency Center was opened at 1580 North Litchfield Road in Goodyear as an extension of the emergency department of Maryvale Samaritan. The center offers emergency outpatient services, radiology, clinical laboratory procedures, EKG facilities, and respiratory therapy to west side residents. In its first year of operation, this outpatient treatment center served more than 4,600 patients. The medical staff consists of advance life support physicians, nurses, technicians, and intermediate emergency medical technicians (IEMenTs). The intermediate emergency medical technicians cooperate with and complement the work of fire departments and other emergency services. The center is supervised by a community advisory board consisting of 15 representatives from local business and government. The critically ill or injured are air-lifted from the center to the hospital of their choice.

Most of the hospitals offered pediatric care, and some of the majors had floors or sections dedicated to this purpose. But there was no children's hospital.

In 1980 the medical specialists who were members of the county's pediatric society invited some leading community figures to an organizational meeting. The pediatricians, led by their president, Dr. David Trump, presented some very compelling arguments to support their plan for a freestanding hospital for the treatment of children.

Such an institution, it was argued, would bring all the specialists in the Valley together, and would eliminate some of the existing duplication in the Valley's general hospitals. There would, they said, be an overall reduction in the cost of pediatric care and an improvement in the quality of care which could be provided.

At the close of the meeting, Doctor Trump asked the non-medical community members in attendance if they would support an effort to create a children's hospital. Allen Rosenberg, one of those present, says, "Practically everyone present held up a hand because it was like quarrelling with the abolition of sin or motherhood to refuse to be concerned about the needs of the children."

On July 31, 1980, the Phoenix Children's Hospital was incorporated. Twelve prominent community-minded individuals were named to the board of directors. They were Allen L. Rosenberg; Dr. Daniel Cloud, past president, American Medical Association; H. Jerome Lewkowitz of the law firm of Rawlins, Burrus and Lewkowitz; Paul Eckstein, a partner in the law firm of Brown and Bain; George Lee, president of Lee Development Company; Orme Lewis, Jr., partner in Applewhite, Laflin and Lewis; Diane McCarthy, Arizona Corporation Commissioner; George W. Reeve, president of George W. Reeve Enterprises and former executive vice president of Del E. Webb Corporation; Edwin Van Brunt, vice president, APS; pediatricians Fred Ruskin and Herbert Winograd; and Ed Wren, vice president of Southwest Forest Industries. Lewkowitz was named secretary, Dr. Cloud, president, and Rosenberg, chairman.

Rosenberg came to Phoenix from Los Angeles in 1933. After a successful career in the grain business, he held responsible executive positions with the Guaranty Bank of Phoenix, the Bank of Scottsdale and the Pioneer Bank of Arizona, retiring in 1974 as director and vice-chairman of the Great Western Bank and Trust Company. He had served on the Phoenix City Council, the Phoenix Municipal Aeronautics Board, the Phoenix Symphony Association; had been president of the Phoenix Chamber of Commerce, was a life Thunderbird, and had been deeply involved in many other civic activities. At the time of this first meeting he was serving as executive director of the Arizona Community Foundation.

Rosenberg became chairman of a committee he describes as "without portfolio, to explore the possibilities of establishing a children's hospital." He says, "When we found out it would cost between $30 and $70 million to build a freestanding hospital, we abandoned that approach as beyond the community's financial ability."

The available alternative was to locate the new Children's Hospital on the campus of some existing hospital.

All the hospitals in the area were contacted. Rosenberg says four expressed a definite interest in the program. These were Good Samaritan, St. Joseph's, Phoenix Memorial, and Phoenix Baptist.

Rosenberg said, "I was acquainted with all of the hospital administrators and had many friends on the various hospitals' boards of directors or trustees. We wanted to be totally independent, to have our own board of directors and our own medical staff. In my preliminary discussions with the administrators at these four institutions they appeared willing and anxious to meet our terms and cooperate."

Rosenberg and members of the ad hoc committee he represented did not want the responsibility of choosing between any of the hospitals in the event all four made similarly attractive offers.

A so-called "blue ribbon" committee was appointed consisting of Rod J. McMullin, former general manager of the Salt River Project and a former state senator; former Governor Jack Williams; Secretary of State Rose Mofford; Dallas Smith of the Dallas Smith Transport Company; Dr. M. B. Bayless, a psychologist; Bill Shover, director of Community Affairs for *The Republic and Gazette*; and Shirley Agnos, executive secretary of the Arizona Academy. Major General Carl Schneider, U.S.A.F. retired, was retained to build the matrix to assist in the evaluation of the contracts offered and the facilities available.

The committee held public hearings, visited all the institutions to inspect the offered facilities, and after careful deliberation announced the new Children's Hospital would be located on the campus and in the buildings of Good Samaritan Medical Center.

The Children's Hospital filed a request for a Certificate of Need with the Central Arizona Health Systems Agency. Before the matter could be heard, Doctor Paul Bergeson, head of pediatrics at Good Samaritan, and Doctor Mel Cohen, head of pediatrics at St. Joseph's, requested a private meeting with Rosenberg. They explained that no matter what the ultimate location of the Children's Hospital, they wanted to work together, if this would be acceptable to the board of the Children's Hospital. Rosenberg took the problem to David Reed, president and chief executive officer of Samaritan Health Service.

Rosenberg was anxious to have the facilities ready and an acceptable staff in place before the Certificate of Need hearings. Reed agreed to provide the necessary support in the event Dr. Cohen wanted to come over to Good Samaritan and help with the preparations. Dr. Cohen and six members of the pediatrics staff at St. Joseph's elected to move to Good Samaritan.

At the Certificate of Need hearing before the Central Arizona Health Systems Agency, a number of witnesses spoke in opposition to the Children's Hospital request. They took the position that the pediatric departments in the existing hospitals were adequately serving the public need. Rosenberg says, "The committee was decimated by illnesses and absences. When it came decision time, only three members of the original group participated. They ruled against us."

The three doctors and nine lay persons serving on the board of directors of the Children's Hospital were deeply disappointed. The Valley's leading pediatricians who had initiated the effort believed the CAHSA decision was wrong. The lay persons, most of whom were community leaders, agreed.

Rosenberg was told that if any existing hospital would dedicate the required number of beds from its existing authorization, the establishment of the Children's Hospital would not require CAHSA authorization.

Samaritan Medical Center agreed to divest itself of 71 beds in the new tower buildings. The Children's Hospital was granted a charter by the State Department of Health Services. The facility was opened on September 18, 1983 and, according to Rosenberg, has been operating at full capacity since that date.

The Phoenix Children's Hospital has developed an affiliation with the University of Arizona Medical Center. With the full approval of President Henry Koffler and Dean Louis Kettel of the College of Medicine, Doctor Vincent Fulginiti, head of pediatrics at the University of Arizona Medical Center, and Dean Kettel will head an advisory committee to assist in the development of services at the Children's Hospital.

CHAPTER 16

Facing the Future

On January 1, 1984, the population of the greater Phoenix metropolitan area exceeded 1.5 million. People were moving to the Sun Belt in increasing numbers. The heavy industries — automobiles, steel, coal — were playing a diminishing role in the nation's economic growth. There were bold predictions that by the year 2010 the population of greater Phoenix would exceed that of any other city in the United States.

Supporters of this optimistic outlook argue that all the necessary resources are present. There is more than adequate land space, the demonstrated ability of Arizona's public utilities to meet the demand for energy, a supply of municipal/industrial water soon to be augmented by importation from the Colorado River, central location in the growing Rocky Mountain region, and an easily expandable transportation system, consisting of a healthy mix of transcontinental railroads, airlines and highways.

One important aspect of this potential growth possibility was overlooked or underplayed; the unquestioned excellence of the health care facilities in place, providing superior medical care to both the resident population and the growing number of patients referred to the specialty facilities in Phoenix by their doctors throughout the Rocky Mountain region.

The 18 not-for-profit community hospitals and the four owned by "for-profit" corporations in Maricopa County had a total of 5,283 beds. The county and state governments, in three institutions, had 781 beds for the treatment of prisoners, children, and the indigent. There were 170 beds for private mental patients and 693 in the State Hospital for mental patients.

At St. Joseph's, a $60 million program for expansion and modernization had been completed. Working with the Phoenix architectural firm of Varney, Sexton and Sydnor, and Health Facilities Systems of Glendale, California, provision was made for a new nursing unit to contain 202 patient beds (most of them replacements for beds in the outmoded patient rooms in the main hospital building), an ancillary services building to house radiology, nuclear medicine, physical medicine, laboratories, operating rooms, the emergency department, pharmacy, food services, central processing, central stores, and other services, an outpatient care center, a multi-level 1,250 car parking structure, and extensive remodeling of the main hospital area.

St. Luke's Hospital, with its expanded facilities, was rapidly becoming recognized as a tertiary care hospital — a leader in preventive medicine and preventive cardiology.

Good Samaritan's 770-bed Medical Center, with all of its ancillary service buildings, was opened. The Phoenix Children's Hospital was in operation. Thunderbird Samaritan had opened its new facilities in the northwest quadrant. (In December, 1982, Lincoln Health Resources, parent holding company for John C. Lincoln Hospital and Health Center, withdrew from the joint Lincoln-Samaritan venture and sold its interest to Samaritan.)

John C. Lincoln had more than its quota of eminently qualified specialists and services. The operation of the emergency room facilities had earned national recognition.

Three of these major hospitals — St. Joseph's, St. Luke's, and Good Samaritan — were located within a two-mile radius of each other.

Community support and aggressive management, population growth and new facilities at Scottsdale Memorial Hospital had greatly increased that community's ability to provide needed health care.

At the far western edge of the Valley, Boswell Memorial Hospital served the needs of the people in those growing retirement communities of Sun City and Sun City West.

A greatly expanded Maricopa County General Hospital on East Roosevelt provided excellent service for the indigent. The hospital's burn unit was considered one of the best in the nation.

That first study of community health needs directed by Hamilton had suggested the three then-existing general hospitals — St. Luke's, St. Joseph's, and Good Samaritan — should be relocated on a single campus in Central Phoenix. That proposal never received any serious consideration because of the intense independence of the three institutions and the significant differences among their constituent supporters.

In 1980 Samaritan Health Service created the Medical Center Redevelopment Corporation (non-profit) to master plan the area bounded by Seventh Street on the west, 13th Street on the east, McDowell Road on the north, and the future Papago Expressway on the south.

Business and neighborhood leaders, together with representatives of SHS, accepted the responsibility to promote the redevelopment of this area, approximately 100 acres, coordinate the efforts with the City of Phoenix, undertake ongoing market analysis, select developers and contractors, and, if necessary, acquire additional property.

In January of 1981, MCRC was granted "master developer" status by the City of Phoenix. The board of MCRC consists of seven community leaders and seven SHS representatives. Property acquired is being sold to developers at cost. Planned for completion within the next ten years, the total project will include a blend of multi-family housing, housing for the elderly and disabled, parks and open spaces, extended care facilities, new and expanded retail services, medical research and development facilities, medical and corporate offices and a hotel.

The Samaritan Park Medical Building and the Arizona Health Plan's new administrative support services building were completed in 1982. MCRC will not make a profit from these operations and will not directly own, improve, or develop real estate within the area.

The expansion of facilities through merger and construction, and the extension of services to rural areas, created management problems for Samaritan Health Service. The for-profit subsidiaries and the need to increase charitable contributions added to the complexity. As a result of the mergers, the board of trustees had been enlarged to accommodate representatives from Maryvale, Glendale, and the East Valley.

As early as 1971, Robert Roe, a member of that enlarged board, had observed that a 40-member governing body, meeting four times a year, could not adequately supervise management. In response, the board had been divided into separate specialized task forces assigned to oversee a particular phase of the operation. This resulted in some improvement, but there was still overlapping and duplication.

In 1976 long-time board chairman Harold Divelbess resigned to accept emeritus status and Earl Bimson was elected chairman. James F. Henderson, a partner in the firm of Gust, Rosenfeld, Divelbess and Henderson, was named to the board, continuing the representation of this pioneer legal firm founded by Joseph Kibbey. In 1979 Ronald H. Warner, long-time board member, was elected chairman to replace Earl Bimson.

To provide more effective management and supervision, the trustees adopted a plan of reorganization in 1981.

A new holding company, SamCor, was created to operate three subsidiary companies — Samaritan Health Service, DynaCor, and Samaritan Medical Foundation. The 48 community volunteers serving as Samaritan Health Service trustees were reassigned according to their particular interest and expertise.

Samaritan Health Service was given full responsibility for the operation of hospitals and other health care facilities and programs.

The for-profit divisions were united under DynaCor.

Samaritan Medical Foundation was made solely responsible for soliciting philanthropic donations and procuring grants from both the private and public sector.

Samaritan Health Service owns four general hospitals: Good Samaritan Medical Center on the central campus in Phoenix, Desert Samaritan Hospital and Health Center in the East Valley, Maryvale Samaritan Hospital in the West Valley, and Thunderbird Samaritan Hospital at 5555 West Thunderbird Road in Glendale. All of the physical plants are new, modern, and designed to provide efficient operation and maximum service to the patients.

SHS operates Samaritan East Valley Emergency Center, Samaritan West Valley Emergency Center, Pleasant Valley Community Medical Center, and is contract manager for the Grand Canyon Clinic, White Mountain Community Hospital and Page Hospital. Desert Samaritan Hospital operates the Ahwatukee Family Practice Center. AirEvac, which in 1983 transported more than 2,000 critically ill patients to Valley hospitals, is supervised by SHS.

Harry J. Cavanagh, prominent Phoenix lawyer, is chairman of the Samaritan Health Service board of directors and David A. Reed is president.

DynaCor operates nine businesses, including a printing company, a commercial laundry for hospitals, nursing homes, a computing and data processing center, a financial service corporation, and a financial acceptance corporation. Two subsidiaries offer assistance in the management of medical practices and in the design, maintenance, and repair of technical equipment. All after-tax profit is used to reduce the cost of health services to the community. William T. Hicks, CEO of Western Electric, is chairman of the board, and Dan L. Dearen, president.

Samaritan Medical Foundation has implemented a major capital gifts program which has raised more than four million dollars to reduce health care costs, and sponsors the Arizona Biltmore Samaritan LPGA Pro-Am Tournament, which has proven to be a substantial fund raiser. L. B. "Lou" Jolly is chairman and Stuart R. Smith, executive vice-president.

When Morris came to Phoenix in 1953, following the tradition established by J. O. Sexson, he became an active participant in community affairs. He joined the Phoenix Kiwanis Club which J. O. Sexson had helped to organize and whose members over the years had contributed so greatly to the Good Samaritan Hospital. Kiwanis Club presidents Wesley Knorpp, Lorel Stapley, J. O. Sexson, Frank L. Snell, Fred G. Holmes, Richard O. Lewis and Delmer Drinen have all served on the hospital's board of trustees. Eventually Steve Morris was elected president of that Kiwanis Club. He was named to the Charter Review Committee and the Planning Commission for the City of Phoenix. He served as trustee, president and chairman of the American Hospital Assocation. He is a Fellow of the American College of Hospital Administrators and the recipient in 1971 of the Gerald B. Lambert Award for his contributions to improve patient care and cost containment.

It is impossible to overestimate the impact of Steve Morris on the health care provider industry nationwide. The hospital system established here in Phoenix under the Morris leadership is being copied in many other states.

The corporate reorganization undertaken by the trustees in 1981 was done to streamline administration. The trustees believed it would increase accountability by requiring both DynaCor and the Foundation to justify their continued existence. There was an additional reason. The trustees and Morris were looking ahead. The national expenditure for health care in the early '60s had been about six percent of the GNP. By 1980 this figure had risen to almost 11 percent of GNP — $350 billion a year. There was considerable public complaint about the increase and the hospitals were being blamed.

As a result of the federal programs of Medicare and Medicaid, hospital patient loads had increased tremendously. But on Medicare and Medicaid admissions, the goverment paid on average only about 85 percent of the actual cost.

Large corporate employers had offered extremely generous health care plans in order to attract workers and the increased costs became a major problem for corporate management.

Hospital's plants have a useful life of only about 15 years; expensive rehabilitation is required at the end of that period.

The industrial bond mechanism, which had provided most of the money for hospital construction and expansion in the '70s, was being questioned by Congress. The giant for-profit chains, with their ready access to investment capital, posed a serious threat to the continued existence of independent hospitals.

The SamCor trustees commenced to examine the possibility of amalgamation or merger with other hospital groups throughout the country. It was hoped that if such a plan could be implemented, the total resources of the not-for-profit hospitals would, perhaps, provide a solution for the unquestioned need to find new capital for construction and rehabilitation.

SamCor became affiliated with two other regional not-for-profit multi-hospital systems to form the Health Network of America (HNA). The other founding members were Lutheran Hospital Society of Southern California and Metropolitan Hospitals Inc. of Portland, Oregon.

Unfortunately, progress was slow and by January, 1984, the Samaritan system and all other not-for-profit hospitals in the United States faced a threatening future.

At the University of California, Los Angeles, School for Public Health Professor Joseph Coyne published findings declaring that one of every four not-for-profit hospitals was running at a loss. He predicted it was only a matter of time before the not-for-profits would have to seek additional capital, either by selling stock to the general public in for-profit subsidiaries or by merger.

John C. Bedrosian, co-founder of Los Angeles based National Medical Enterprises said, "In an economic sense, a 19th Century institution is suddenly being catapulted into the 20th Century."

In Arizona the AHCCCS system — the state's answer to Medicaid — was in deep trouble. There were millions of dollars of cost overruns. McAuto, the private corporation selected by the Governor to administer the program, blamed the Legislature. The Governor was charged with being lax in his oversight. The Attorney General demanded an audit. McAuto withdrew. The taxpayers will eventually make up the deficiencies.

The federal government, with the announced objective of reducing payments to hospitals, adopted a new reimbursement system designated DRG, Diagnostic Related Groupings.

More than 50 percent of the patients being admitted to the Samaritan hospitals were coming in as Medicare or AHCCCS sponsored. It was easy to see the handwriting on the wall. If 50 percent of the hospitals' patients were being billed at less than cost, the loss would have to be made up by charging other patients more. To complicate the problem, the insurance companies and employee benefit groups were demanding similar discounts.

The Samaritan system was contributing approximately $4 million a year to medical education in the greater Phoenix area, providing more than $8 million a year in charity hospital care and absorbing about $30 million annually in bad debts and allowances created by Medicare and other patients who could not or would not pay their bills. A number of vital health care services, such as the Kidney Dialysis Center, the Spinal Injury Service and Air-Evac, were not breaking even.

In some eastern states legislation was passed authorizing newly established commissions to set the fees for hospital service. In Arizona a coalition of private employers, headed by the high tech companies Sperry, Motorola and Garrett, commenced circulation of petitions to put legislation on the ballot in November which would establish a super powerful state agency with authority to set hospital rates for all services, to put ceilings on the charges which could be made by laboratories and doctors in group practice.

The situation reached crisis proportions when the federal government passed legislation greatly restricting the use of industrial bonds, thus destroying the independent hospitals' principal method for raising capital funds.

The SamCor board formed a task force to investigate alternatives and develop a strategy best calculated to permit the hospitals to continue to operate at the lower revenues and, at the same time, offer those vital services which had never been self-supporting.

The task force quickly discovered the problems were not unique to Arizona. In some eastern states, where rates were controlled by legislation, hospitals had been forced to reduce services. In Omaha, Nebraska St. Joseph's Hospital, an institution owned by the Catholic Church which is also the teaching facility for Creighton Medical School, sold out to a for-profit chain. The proceeds from the sale were used to establish a medical foundation and the foundation income has been dedicated to subsidizing the medical education program of Creighton University.

Confronted with the probability that the population of the greater Phoenix area would double in the next 15 years, it was estimated the Samaritan system would need at least $200 million in new capital to maintain, rehabilitate and construct new physical facilities. In mid-June, 1984, the task force was preparing its report for presentation to the full SamCor board.

On June 22, 1984, two members of the SamCor board who had been aware of the task force operation — one was a member of the task force — told *The Arizona Republic* that Stephen Morris was secretly planning to sell the Samaritan hospital system and its related enterprises to a for-profit hospital corporation.

The community at large, having no understanding of the threats confronting the not-for-profit hospital systems, exhibited considerable shock and indignation.

Governor Bruce Babbitt condemned the plan and declared he would do everything in his power to prevent such a sale. There were whispered stories that Morris had made a secret deal with a potential purchaser and would be paid $5 million for his part in the transaction.

When Stephen Morris came to Good Samaritan as an administrative resident in 1953 the population of Phoenix was 331,770. The appraised value of the 220-bed hospital plant was less than $1 million. At the beginning of 1984 the replacement value of those health care facilities administered by SamCor and held in trust for the community was at least $400 million. The value of the assets had been increased by the skill of the Morris management. Charitable contributions over this period amounted to less than five percent of the increased value. At least two other hospitals in the Phoenix area had been approached by the for-profit chains and it was obvious to members of the task force that if Samaritan sold first it would receive a premium price.

On June 25, 1984, under attack from all sides, Stephen Morris decided to resign as chief executive officer of SamCor. His decision was based in part on a belief that if he removed himself passions would cool. He thought the community and the SamCor board could then objectively examine the alternatives to be presented by the task force and whatever strategy was finally adopted would be more acceptable to the community. The Sam-Cor board accepted Morris' resignation and named David Reed, president and chief executive officer of Samaritan Health Service, his replacement as chief executive officer. James Simmons, Chairman of the Board, United Bank of Arizona and a member of the SamCor board of directors, replaced Morris as chairman of the board.

* *

In his remarkable epistle to the Romans, St. Paul said, "I consider that the sufferings of this present time are not worth comparing with the glory that is to be revealed to us."

The community hospitals which have served so faithfully and so well throughout the history of the republic were born of struggle and sacrifice. No one can accurately predict the future. UCLA's Professor Coyne may be correct in his assumptions and economic reality may dim the divisions now existing between the non-profit and the for-profit hospitals. But, judging by past performance, we can be confident the basic hospital system in the United States will survive.

The challenges of tomorrow appear to be quite different from the problems of the past. Certainly the facilities are greatly expanded, the dollar amounts are larger, the quality of professional help tremendously improved, but the task and the goals remain the same.

When Sisters Mary Peter and Mary Alacoque solicited the help of that pioneer business community to start a hospital, they were making an affirmative response to the needs of others. Personal tragedy inspired the Reverend J. W. Atwood to build St. Luke's, a tubercular sanitorium. Lulu Clifton, who dedicated her life in answer to our Lord's instructions to teach, to preach and to heal, was fulfilling an earlier commitment. The men and women who worked with the little Desert Mission in Sunnyslope and ultimately built the great general hospital named John C. Lincoln were motivated to help those desperately in need.

The problems confronting us in 1984 will be overcome by individuals preserving and protecting the legacy of courage, compassion, self-sacrifice and hope bequeathed to us by Lulu Clifton, the Sisters of Mercy, the Episcopal priest, and those citizens who joined with them in joyful obedience of our Lord's instruction, "Thou shalt love thy neighbor as thyself."

For all of them, these words of Luke the Physician were written:

Lord, now lettest thou thy servant, depart in peace,
according to thy word.
For mine eyes have seen thy salvation,
Which thou has prepared before the face of all people;
To be a light to lighten the Gentiles and to be the
glory of thy people Israel.

APPENDIX

Honor Roll

The men and women of the greater Phoenix community who over the years have contributed their time and their talent in the service of their neighbors as members of the boards of directors of the Deaconess Hospital, Good Samaritan Hospital, Samaritan Health Service, Samaritan Medical Foundation, DynaCor and SamCor:

James Aldrich
Guy Alsap
George Anderson
A. L. Baker
W. B. Barkley
M. O. Best
William A. Betts
Earl Bimson
Marion K. Bolin
Rev. George Boss
Elmer Bradley
William Brainard
Albert E. Breland, Jr.
Lee Brown
Yvette Ward Bryant
Kenneth H. Buckwald
Robert P. Bulla
George Busey
Wilford Cardon
B. F. Carter
Harry J. Cavanagh
Mr. L. H. Chalmers
John H. W. Champion
Herman Chanen

Gordon C. Chapman
Gene Cheuvront
Lloyd B. Christy
Vernon Clark
Lulu I. Clifton
Donald Cline
Daniel T. Cloud
Jack M. Cochran
L. W. Coggins
C. E. "Pep" Cooney
L. J. Cox
Susan Cratty
Robert O. Cummins
Bernard David
Thomas E. Davis
Clayton Dean
Dan L. Dearen
Ed Dee
O. Mark DeMichele
John Dennett
Harold Diamond
Ike Diamond
Harold Divelbess
Herbert Dozoretz

Delmer Drinen
Alfred J. Duncan
Robert Easley
Paul Eckstein
J. C. Elms
Ruth Ellbogen
Berger Erickson
J. A. Farnsworth, Jr.
O. S. Fees
H. L. Fletcher
Richard O. Flynn
Ralph Goitia
C. W. Goodman
Harry T. Goss
Hugh Gruwell
William Guffey
John L. Gust
Eldon B. Hamblin
Guy M. Hanner
Mrs. Lois Hansen
Rev. Ray C. Harker
Clifford J. Harris
Richard J. Haynes
Moses B. Hazeltine
Sherman Hazeltine
Daniel H. Heller
M. Henderson
James F. Henderson
David E. Heywood
William T. Hicks
Irwin G. "Pete" Homes
Margaret Hulse
Hardy A. Ingham
J. A. R. Irvine
Patricia L. Jackson
Kenneth A. Jacuzzi
C. C. Jenkins
L. B. "Lou" Jolly
Glenn E. Johnson
A. F. Jones
Richard W. Kane
Forence Kelly
John S. Kerr
Frank M. Kilgard
Max Klass
Wesley W. Knorpp
George Kokalis
Pamela Grant Korf
Edgar L. Korrick
Franklin D. Lane
Warren Langfitt
James Laugharn
Golder Lawrence
Peter A. Lendrum

A. W. Leonard
Burton J. Lewin
Delbert R. Lewis
Richard O. Lewis
John C. Lincoln
John F. Long
John D. Loper
Walter Lucking
Eddie Lynch
Roger Lyon
Gerald Marshall
Diane B. McCarthy
Gloria McCarvel
B. F. McGough
William G. Mennen
Rev. R. N. Merrill
George W. Mickle
Frank Middleton
A. W. Miller
E. W. Montgomery
Stephen M. Morris
Arthur R. Nelson
J. C. Norton
Rev. Edward P. O'Rear
Glenn D. Overman
Dwight Patterson
William G. Payne
Byron Peck
D. J. Peters
W. D. Pew
J. C. Phillips
Robert A. Price
Joanne Ralston
Cecil Ravenswood
David A. Reed
John Rhodes
William B. Robey
S. J. Rogers
Judy Rolle
Gene Rouse
Robert B. Rowe
Jon P. Rubach
Willis Sanderson
Raymond F. Schaeffer
D. I. Schildkraut
Warwick Scott
Arlena E. Seneca
J. O. Sexson
Jacob Shapiro
James P. Simmons
H. C. Simonson
Paul L. Singer
Frank O. Smith
Noel G. Smith

Stuart R. Smith
Alice Snell
Frank Snell
Frank S. Tolone
Rev. Frank Toothaker
Don B. Tostenrud
K. S. Townsend
Patricia A. Tully
Clarence R. Wagner
Neil O. Ward
Ronald H. Warner
Morrison Warren
Jack W. Whiteman
Charles R. Whitney
H. B. Wilkinson
Russell Williams
Wayne H. Wood
Joe E. Woods
Levi Young
Woodson C. Young
B. F. Youngker
Martha J. Youngker
Phillip Zabba

BIBLIOGRAPHY

Barnes, Will C. *Arizona Place Names.* Tucson, University of Arizona, 1935.

Biographies, Arizona Elected Officials. Phoenix, Arizona State Department of Library and Archives.

Christy, Lloyd B. *Life History of COL William Christy, By His Son, Lloyd B. Christy.* 14 pages.

Coleman, Claude C. *Doctors of the Gadsden Purchase.*

Conners, Jo. *Who's Who In Arizona.* Tucson, Press of *The Arizona Daily Star,* 1913.

Fireman, Bert M. *Arizona, Historic Land.* New York, Alfred A. Knopf, Inc., 1982.

Hendricks, W. O. *M. H. Sherman: A Pioneer Developer of the Southwest.* Corona Del Mar, California, Sherman Foundation, 1971.

"Los Angeles Corral," *The Westerners.* Brand Book XIII.

Maxwell, George Hebard. *The Argonauts of Golden California.* A biography of his father, John Morgan Maxwell.

Maxwell, George Hebard. Personal handwritten diary.

Maxwell, George Hebard. *Tombstone Luck.* Autobiography, original handwritten manuscript.

McClintock, James Harvey. *Arizona*. Chicago, S. J. Clarke Publishing Company, 1915.

Murphy, Merwin L. *William John Murphy and the Building of the Arizona Canal*. Alhambra, California, 1974.

Palmer, Erroll Payne. *Personal Autobiography, 1876-1960*.

Palmer, Ralph F. *Doctors On Horseback*. Mesa, Arizona, McCarter, 1979.

Peplow, Edward Hadduck. *History of Arizona*. New York, Lewis Historical Publishing Company, Inc., 1958.

Pollock, Paul W. "Profiles of Prominent Personalities," *American Biographical Encyclopedia*. Phoenix, Paul W. Pollock, 1981.

Pollock, Paul W. *Arizona's Men of Achievement*. Phoenix, Paul W. Pollock, 1958-64.

Portrait and Biographical Record of Arizona. Chicago, Chapman Publishing Company, 1901.

Quebbeman, Frances E. *Medicine in Territorial Arizona*. Phoenix, Arizona Historical Foundation, 1966.

Shadegg, Stephen C. *Century One*. The story of man's progress in Central Arizona. 1969.

Shields, Hazel. *Pioneer Nurses of Arizona*. Recollections of Bertha Case.

Sloan, Richard E. *History of Arizona*. Phoenix, Record Publishing Company, 1930.

Thomas, Margaret, "Christy Ranch, History Holds Memories," *The Arizona Republic,* August 8, 1961.

"What George H. Maxwell Has Done For Arizona," Editorial, *Arizona Republican,* May 22, 1907.

Who's Who In America. Volume 18, 1933-34.

Wilson, Roscoe G. *Pioneer Cattlemen of Arizona*. Phoenix, McGrew Commercial Printery, 1951.

Wyllys, Rufus Kay. *Men and Women of Arizona, Past and Present*. Phoenix, Pioneer Publishing Company, 1940.

Miscellaneous Sources:

Arizona Directory Company Directories
Arizona State Nurses' Association Yearbook 1927-28
Board of Supervisors Annual Report, Maricopa County
Bell's Directory of Phoenix and the Salt River Valley
Brochures and publications, Good Samaritan Hospital
Buck's City Directory
Department of Labor Census information
Good Samaritan Hospital Board of Directors Meetings
Phoenix Directory Company City Directories
Records of the Arizona Corporation Commission
Records of the Arizona Hospital Association
Records of the Maricopa County Assessor's Office
Records of the Maricopa County Recorder's Office
Records and journals of the Methodist Church
Salt River Project Museum Records
Skinners Directory
Third Annual Report of the Reclamation Service, prepared by the
    U.S. Geological Survey, 1903-04.

Interviews were conducted with the following individuals:
Loretta Hanner Bardewyck, Vurlyne Boan, Dr. L. D. Beck, Lucille
Brown, Robert Creighton, Milt Coggins, Carolyn Durkin, Edith
Sexson Faville, Carol Goodson, Mary Jane Knorpp Harwood,
John Hughes, Dr. Paul Jarrett, Orme Lewis, Brian Lockwood,
Grace Middlebrook, Mrs. T. Morley, Joe Prekup, Dr. and Helen
Shackelford, Dr. Paul Singer, Frank Snell, Dr. E. Henry Running,
Joe Ralston, and Dr. Dermont Melick.

INDEX

Clifton, Lulu, 1, 3, 9, 14, 17-29, 34-36, 44-46, 49, 52-55, 75, 124, 164
Cloud, Daniel, 106, 151
Clyne, Meade, 68
Cocks, Bertrand R., 20, 119
Coggins, Lewis W., 24-25, 34, 45-46, 48, 97, 119, 138
Coggins, Milt, 138
Cohen, Mel, 152
Coles, Loretta, 91
Colley, Marguerite, 95
Colley, W. A., 95
Collins, M. E., 7
Combined Health Resources, 120
Community Council, 101, 115, 119, 129, 145
Comprehensive Health Planning Council, 116-117
Cortez Street, 38
Cowden, E. Ray, 96
Cox, L. J., 46
Coyne, Joseph, 160, 163
Craig, Carlos C., 79
Craig, Walter E., 101, 102, 127
Creasman, James, 127
Creighton Medical School, 162
Crippled Children's Hospital, 77
Cullen, Richard J., 96
Dameron, Logan D., 19, 33, 68, 70
Davidson, Ira, 56
Davis, Arthur P., 11
Davis-Monthan Field, 83
Davis, N. E., 46, 69
Deaconess Hospital of Omaha, 17
Dearen, Dan L., 159
Diehl's, H. A., 39
Dennett, John, Jr., 26, 34, 45-46, 68
Desert Mission Convalescent Hospital, 94-96, 164
Desert Samaritan Hospital, 131-132, 145, 147-148, 158
Diamond, Harold, 73, 110-111
Diamond, Isaac, 73, 97
Diamond's, 81, 94, 128
Dill, Mrs. M. G., 27
Divelbess, Harold, 110-111, 158
Doctors Hospital, 103, 105
Donofrio Confectionery Company, 49, 81
Doran, Reverend John, 113
Dorris-Heyman's, 81, 144
Douglas, James C., 67
Douglas, Lewis W., 50
Dravis, Faith, 61

Drinen, Del, 110, 159
Dunham, H. L. "Doc", 101, 112-113
Frank Dunning, 132
DynaCor, 149, 158-159
Dysart, Lewis, 70
Dysart, Palmer, 61
Dysart, S. A., 24
East Lake Park, 9
East Valley Health Service Center, 148
Eckstein, Paul, 151
Eddy, Mary Baker, 75
Edens, J. B., 137
Ehrenberg, 21
Ehrlich, Joe, 106
Ehrlich, Lee, 106
Eisele, Ed, 21
Eisenbeiss, Mrs. John, 113
Ellis, Helen, 69-70
Ellis, William C., 59, 68-69
Ellis Building, 59
Elms, J. C., 73
Elsik, Margaret, 65
Episcopal Church, 119-120
Episcopal Diocese of Arizona, 119
Erhardt, Freida, 63
Erickson's Tract, 94
Fahlen, Frederick T., 69
Falcon Field, 83
Farnsworth, Stan, 113
Father of Arizona, 30
Faville, Edith Sexson Brown, 38-39, 47, 60, 88
Faville, F. A., 88
Felch, Harry J., 70
Fennemore, Benita, 91
Firestone, 32
First Methodist Church, 17-24, 28, 89-90
First National Bank of Arizona, 110, 113
First Presbyterian Church, 95
Fisher, Reverend Robert S., 22, 26
Fitzhugh, Ed, 113
Forbes, J. Robert, 104
Ford Hotel, 21-22, 39
Fort Huachuca, 83
Foster, Fred, 132
Fowler, Benjamin A., 12-14, 22, 41
Fremont, John C., 6
Frissell, Ben Pat, 79, 84, 113
Fulginiti, Vincent, 153
Gabrielson, Rosamond, 65
Gadsden Purchase, 30
Gammage, Grady, 62-64

U.S.S. Arizona, 83
Udall, Nick, 88
Universal Development Corporation
of California, 105
University of Arizona, 64, 121, 127
University of Arizona Medical Center,
153
University of Redlands, 48
Utleys, 49, 58, 60
Valley Bank of Phoenix, 11, 24, 29,
32-33, 39, 45, 49, 72-73
Valley National Bank, 7, 59, 72-73, 86,
113, 124, 134
VanBrunt, Edwin, 151
Varney, Sexton and Sydnor, 156
Verde River, 4-5, 9-10
Visiting Nurses, 101
Vivian, Charles S., 58, 69, 79
Vosburgh, C. O., 89
Vulture Mine, 4
Walker Party, 4
Wallingford, V. O., 35
Ward, William H., 19
Warner, Ronald H., 158
Warrenburg, Clarence, 61
Washington University (St. Louis), 99
Washington Women's Club, 95
Watkins, W. Warner, 70, 84
Wayne, John, 141
Weaver, Pauline, 2
Webb, Del E., 53, 124
Westward Ho Hotel, 72, 82, 144
Wetzler, J. Charles, 113
White Mountain Community
Hospital, 137, 140, 158
Whiting, Spencer D., 58
Wickenburg, 14, 18, 75
Wickenburg, Henry, 4
Wilkinson, Henry Bannister, 24-28,
32, 34, 39, 43, 47
Willard Hotel, 30
Williams, Bill, 2
Williams Field, 83-85, 130
Williams, Henry, 61
Williams, Jack, 89, 93, 113, 118, 152
Williams, Marilla B., 19, 26, 33
Wilpitz, Roland, 132
Wilson, Thina, 56
Winograd, Herbert, 151
Woern, W. H., 84
Wolfe, Emma, 46, 53, 56
Womack, P. W., 86
Women's suffrage, 31
Woodman, Tommy, 79

Woolworth Company, E. F., 110
Wren, Ed, 151
Wylie, Winfred, 67
Yaeger, Lucille, 56
YMCA, 22-23, 26, 39-40, 42-43, 45-48,
95, 101
Young, Johnny, 122
Young, Levi, 34
Youngker, B. F., 106, 110-111
Zorne, Gertrude, 124